CHILDREN AND INDUSTRY

The textile area of the North-west, including places referred to in the text

Marjorie Cruickshank

CHILDREN AND INDUSTRY

CHILD HEALTH AND WELFARE
IN NORTH-WEST TEXTILE TOWNS
DURING THE NINETEENTH CENTURY

*Manchester
University Press*

Published by
Manchester University Press
Oxford Road, Manchester M13 9PL

British Library cataloguing in publication data

Cruickshank, Marjorie
Children and industry.
1. Children in Great Britain – History
I. Title
942.007   HG792.G7

ISBN 0–7190–0809–3

The publishers gratefully acknowledge the
assistance of the Pasold Research Fund
towards the cost of publication

Computerised Phototypesetting
by G.C. Typeset Ltd., Bolton, Greater Manchester

Printed and bound in Great Britain by
Biddles Ltd, Guildford and King's Lynn

CONTENTS

LIST OF ILLUSTRATIONS

ACKNOWLEDGEMENTS

Many people have helped me in the preparation of this book. In conception the topic owes much to early discussion with Dr Kathleen Farrar and Dr John Pickstone of the University of Manchester Institute of Science and Technology.

In the course of research I have been indebted to hospital administrators, to archivists and to local librarians who have made records available. In particular, I have been assisted by Miss Jean Ayton, archivist at Manchester Central Library, and Miss Pauline Leech, archivist at Manchester Royal Infirmary. During the writing of my script I have received generous help from Dr H. W. S. Francis, of the Department of Community Medicine at the University of Manchester and from Dr William Brockbank, medical historian.

I am grateful to the University of Keele for affording me facilities for research and in particular for a term's leave of absence. I have profited from discussion with colleagues and with my students in the Department of Education. Miss Eileen Beard, Visual Aids Officer in the department, and her assistant, Miss Helen Addams, have given valuable aid with illustrations.

Finally my special thanks are to Miss Vera Holland and Mrs Yvonne Barnett for their patience and efficiency in typing my text.

INTRODUCTION

Our own humane society regards children as its most valued possession. Almost from conception the infant and later the child is the concern of the health and welfare services. Indeed, it is not merely the child's physical well-being which the State considers important. In the words of the White Paper of 1943, the forerunner of the Act which governs English education today, the objective was 'to secure for children a happier childhood and a better start in life . . .'.[1]

Recognition of health as a basic human right is a twentieth-century concept. If it were possible to go back even to the later years of the last century to look at children in the industrial districts, the most startling contrast with our own day would undoubtedly be their physical appearance. We would note the smaller stature and pinched faces, particularly of working children, the unsightly joints and crooked limbs, the scars and open sores, the number of cripples in irons and on crutches and, above all, the prevalence of dirt and discomfort in flea-bitten bodies and infested hair. It is in the physical transformation of children that the term 'silent social revolution' becomes truly meaningful.

The special care for the nurture of children in the mass which we take for granted is relatively new. It has been a result of humanitarian endeavour; it has also been a response to self-interest and, with the diminishing proportion of children in the population, to a realisation of their scarcity. As the young have become more precious and have come to be recognised as the greatest national asset, so the period of childhood has been extended to avoid premature exposure to the physical and psychological strains of the adult world.

In the past children were taken for granted. There were, of course, always swarms of them. Before the industrial revolution it was estimated that a third of the population had not reached their teens, and through most of the nineteenth century births increased at what often seemed an alarming rate. In *The World we have lost* Peter Laslett has described the young in the pre-industrial age.[2] They were everywhere: as babes in arms, as toddlers hanging on to skirts, and as noisy, mischievous children who were put to work as soon as possible. Since their feeding and clothing were a drain on the energies and resources of the labouring population, no time was lost in putting them to useful employment. They learnt 'on the job' on farms and smallholdings, in domestic industry or in the home. For historians they are a silent multitude known only by the record of baptisms and burials and from glimpses in the literature of the times.

Economic necessity was the obvious reason for child labour. Early in the eighteenth century Defoe, investigating the domestic industry of the West Riding, had noted that 'hardly anything above four years old, but its hands are sufficient to itself'.[3] With a tradition of early work it was hardly surprising that local vestries refused outdoor aid for eight-year-olds on the ground that they were able to fend for themselves.

Besides the economic motive there was also the force of 'moral Puritanism', the conviction that youthful high spirits must be curbed early. If children were to be prevented from falling into mischief and crime—and later into a life of indigence and depravity that would make them a burden on society—they must be subdued and accustomed to habits of industry. The principle was applied to rich and poor alike; for the former, childhood was devoted to the drudgery of memory work in 'the untimely culture of the mind';[4] for the latter it was spent in physical toil.

Like earlier forms of labour the factory was seen as a way of 'turning the restless energy of childhood into productive channels'[5] and, as Wesley observed when he saw children at work in an early silk mill, a means of diverting them from the temptations of idleness.[6] Thus children had always been workers; their labour in the fields, the workshop or the home had been taken for granted. Sometimes, of course, they had been overworked. What was new in the industrial revolution was that they were harnessed to power-driven machinery.

Work now took them out of the home and put them increasingly under the control of adults outside family or kin. They became 'hands', summoned and dismissed by the factory bell and disciplined by strangers. It was the excessive labour of children under the factory regime which was to rouse public concern.

The historian of industrial England cannot fail to be conscious of the children of the 'lower orders'. They were visible everywhere in the crowded thoroughfares as sweepers, beggars and pickpockets. They were part of the mass of labourers in the workshops, factories and brickfields and as such appear in the wage registers, in the documentation of inspectors and investigators. Their numbers and occupations are known from the decennial censuses and their mortality statistics from the reports of the Registrar General, where individual life according to actuarial calculations was assessed in monetary terms on a sliding scale according to age. Their conditions of work and educational progress are set out in official publications, their struggles and tribulations are revealed in autobiographies, school log books and contemporary novels, their physical sufferings in dispensary and infirmary records. All in all, there is apparently abundant evidence, statistical and descriptive, collected both by local initiative and by central direction. Of no region is this more true than the textile areas of the North-west. Yet the testimony is far less complete than it seems. Some of the statistical evidence has to be treated with caution. For instance, mortality figures, both before and after registration, were inaccurate. Even at the end of the century many deaths went unrecorded or were wrongly attributed. Statistics of treatment by medical charities are similarly suspect.

Of descriptive evidence too much comes 'from above', from amateurs and so-called experts—including government inspectors and officials. It comes particularly from members of the medical profession, the nineteenth-century health missionaries whose observations on life in the textile towns were often sweepingly condemnatory. Mothers were castigated as 'ignorant', 'negligent', 'wilful', 'careless' and 'stubborn'; their irrationality, apathy and fatalism were deplored; their reliance on instinct and tradition was seen as the greatest barrier to improvement. Alas, we need to know much more about the mothers themselves and the kinsfolk on whom they relied so heavily in order to get beyond the commentary of

professionals. As it is, we rarely hear of them direct; their words and
deeds are overlaid by the interpretation of others. Thus we have mere
glimpses 'from below', from what a near-contemporary called 'the
depressed class of women',[7] wives and mothers whose fears and
feelings we are left to imagine.

In the dramatic growth of the cotton industry women and children
played a significant part. Edward Baines estimated in 1835 that
together they comprised two-thirds of the labour force.[8] Children,
particularly, adapted easily to the new order. They were too young to
share nostalgia for the past, the brooding resentment at the loss of
independence and hatred of a regime which in the words of a local
song kept the worker 'locked up like a bird in a cage'.[9] Docile and
tractable, they submitted to the disciplines of mechanisation and to
training in the new virtues of obedience, regularity and punctuality.

From the early years of the century there were efforts to rescue them
from the most harmful conditions of factory employment: long hours,
unguarded machinery and harsh treatment. By mid-century the
worse excesses had been curbed. Sometimes, however, parents were
more callous than employers, even to the point of defying the law. For
whatever reason—necessity, insecurity or greed—they valued their
offspring in economic terms. The demand for child labour encouraged
a high birth rate. After brief years of dependence children were a
financial asset and an assurance against old age. In the hierarchy of
labour the unskilled worker looked for early returns from his
offspring; the skilled craftsmen, in contrast, could take a longer term
view, could send his children to school and later put them to a trade.

It was the young who were most susceptible to the adverse
conditions of life in the industrial communities. Family poverty,
whether imposed or self-inflicted, bore heavily on them. Always the
distinction was between the respectable poor and the degraded poor.
The former could hope to tide themselves over temporary periods of
slump. Often, when serious misfortune befell them, they struggled in
obscurity and brought their children up as best they could. Hence,
despite the array of statistics of wages and prices, it is difficult to
penetrate to the real poor who kept their sufferings to themselves. In
contrast, revelations about the degraded poor are easily accessible in
the reports of rescue societies and the records of public institutions.
The danger is of gross distortion, and similar perils attend

descriptions of the treatment and care of children at public expense where cases of flagrant abuse attracted notoriety.

It was assumed that there would always be poverty—in the words of the Manchester and Salford District Provident Society, that 'the time will never come when the poor shall cease out of the land'.[10] On the other hand, dirt, equally a scourge and a source of disease, could be eradicated by individual effort. Hence there were constant exhortations to cleanliness, considered the key to health, self-respect, even morality. It was next to godliness. But the crusade could make little advance until, from the middle years of the century, soap and light were more widely available and until municipalities recognised their sanitary responsibilities.

Whatever the particular circumstances of adversity, the young were especially vulnerable. In the words of an official actuary, infants were 'little blossoms which fall to the ground almost as soon as they see light'.[11] Many who survived were diseased and debilitated by rickets, associated particularly with the conditions of the factory districts. Concern for the physical privations of children was left to individuals, and the treatment of infirmities and ailments was a focus of charitable effort within the communities. Local dispensaries were the result of voluntary endeavour. Public authorities, by contrast, confined their attention to the offspring of paupers and vagrants and, through the very form of their provision, made it clear that they were visiting the sins of the parents on them. By the latter part of the century new public health authorities were endeavouring to control disease by sanitary improvements and building isolation hospitals.

There are, however, great gaps in our knowledge of the treatment of children's illness and disease. Evidence other than that from medical authorities and advertisers is scanty. The former castigated all unorthodox practitioners, including homoeopaths and herbalists; in medical journals they ridiculed their presciptions, condemned their failures and called for severe penalties. Universally they denounced those outside the profession as quacks and imposters. Patent medicines, beguiling in their promises of certain cure, had a considerable following, though their cost put them beyond the pockets of most workers' families. Of the cheaper alternatives there is less precise evidence. Druggists were commonly applied to, as in some communities were self-taught herbalists, but we know little of the great mass of itinerant vendors who pedalled their wares or of market-stall holders except by chance reference to the gaping crowds they attracted. Almost as elusive is knowledge of the simple domestic remedies, mentioned occasionally in diaries or dialect tales or gleaned from oral recollections.

Regard for 'the rising generation' by the later Victorians was reflected in further protective legislation and in the extension of compulsory schooling. In theory it was recognised that healthy children were a capital asset; in practice, there was resistance to any move which would undermine parental responsibility.

By the '90s a declining birth rate and evidence of social deterioration heralded a new era in children's welfare. On military as well as economic grounds the young were seen as the country's greatest resource. In the national self-interest they could no longer be neglected. Attention was drawn to the root cause of child disability, malnutrition, and to the need for positive action. Just as early in the century the State's assumption of a measure of responsibility for elementary education had brought extension of its obligations, so in the present century its concern for the physical well-being of children was to take it into new spheres of social service.

The study is divided into broad chronological sections related to the effect of industrial development in the North-west on the children of those whom contemporaries termed the 'labouring poor'. The first, from the end of the eighteenth century to the 1830s, covers the transition from domestic to factory labour; the second, the first half of the Victorian era, relates to the period of rapid industrial and urban expansion, largely unregulated and in its worst aspects tempered only by voluntary initiative; the third, the final decades of the century, brings the first foreboding of the harvest of neglect.

It is not the intention to include middle-class children except by way of contrast. In certain respects, in their food and physical conditions, such children were at an advantage. Often they were more resistant to infection, though their numerous household contacts exposed them to risk. In other respects they were perhaps not favourably placed. Wet nurses, even those provided by the Lying-in Charity, were not always suitable. Nor was it unknown for the monthly nurse to drug the infant with laudanum. By the latter part of the century nurses trained in the Children's Hospital were available for illness in prosperous private families, but in the earlier years, certainly, medical treatment was often of doubtful value. Indeed, within the profession child medicine ranked low until well into the twentieth century. It is therefore not surprising to find references to children rather sparse in the medical journals of the earlier period. In addresses to learned societies, in the cases recorded of hospital practice and in courses of clinical lectures children's ailments and disease were rarely mentioned. There was one exception; from mid-century diphtheria, on account of the difficulty of distinguishing it from croup and scarlet fever, roused interest and discussion.

From her childhood in the industrial North-west the writer has been able to draw on recollections and oral evidence of aspects of life in earlier generations when the textile industry was its life blood and the source of a distinctive culture. The historical investigation was undertaken alongside a team based in the University of Manchester Institute of Science and Technology which was studying medical history in the former Manchester Regional Hospital Board's area. Though the Board's boundaries had extended to outlying regions, the writer confined her enquiries to the textile districts during the period of just over a century, very crudely the years which saw the rise and expansion of the region's major industry before it was to fall away sharply—as had happened already to the silk industry—in the early twentieth century.

ONE

TRANSITION FROM
THE OLD ORDER,
1780–1833

I CHILDREN AND INDUSTRY

Throughout the nineteenth century and well into the twentieth the area from Preston in the east to Oldham in the West, from Clitheroe and Burnley in the north to Macclesfield and Congleton in the south, was dominated by the textile industry. Traditionally linen had been manufactured in districts of west Lancashire, woollens in the Pennine villages and settlements of the east, while in the Cheshire towns to the south the silk industry was well established. In the early eighteenth century many of the communities made a poor impression on outsiders. Defoe, for example, found Rochdale 'so remote, so out of the way and so at the foot of the mountains that we may suppose it would be but little frequented'.[1] Manchester, already associated with the making of fustian (coarse cotton), as were parts of central Lancashire, he described as 'one of the greatest, if not the greatest meer village in England'.[2] In the countryside families combined small-scale farming with manufacture. Usually the father wove the cloth and apprenticed his sons to weaving. The mother and daughters engaged in spinning and in the preliminary processes. Even the youngest children by winding the bobbins were able to make a contribution.

Some communities became wholly dependent on industry. Possibly there were several looms in each house with girls as well as boys put to work. By the age of twelve, as experienced weavers, they were responsible for carrying their own 'cuts' to the middlemen, often a distance of several miles, and for bringing back their weft. In many areas, however, weaving was more highly organised and was concentrated in extensive upper rooms. Meanwhile, despite the changes in spinning, early jennies were sufficiently small to fit in the cottages. It was only with the displacement of the domestic jennies by larger machinery from the closing decades of the eighteenth century that spinning was transferred to factories.

It would be misleading to think of the domestic system in rosy terms. In outlying Pennine areas the cold and the dampness had long been associated with bronchitis and consumption which left many children premature orphans. Parents themselves set their offspring to labour early. In the towns, especially, children were confined in cold, damp cellars where they wove a great variety of cloths: calicoes, nankeens, ginghams, jaconet, checks, dimities, velveteens and fustians. As Dr Thomas Percival of Manchester wrote in 1775, 'love of money stifles the feelings of humanity, and even makes men blind to the very interest they so anxiously pursue'.[3] By the same principle that horses and cattle were spared until they attained strength and vigour, children needed similar respite.

Everywhere the close work affected health and eyesight. Of one family on Marsden Height (later part of Nelson) an observer wrote during a depression in the early nineteenth century, 'They have a desolate lad with them who has bad sight but weaves a little.'[4] Fluctuations in trade caused periods of hardship, and masters who had brought in parish apprentices for their looms during good trade thought nothing of turning them adrift when times were bad.[5]

During prosperous years, the so-called golden age towards the end of the eighteenth century, there was plenty to eat. As Samuel Bamford recalled, his fare in a Middleton weaver's family included dinners of meat and potatoes, meat and broth with oat-cakes and barm dumpling. 'Bagging' in the afternoon was oat-cake with butter, treacle, cheese or milk, and on Sunday morning, to accompany the oat-cakes and butter, there was 'mint or balm tea, sweetened with treacle'.[6] Throughout the area oatmeal, eaten as porridge or made into cakes or bread, known as jannock, was a staple food, though already in the larger towns wheaten bread was commonly baked. Potatoes, for long associated with the Irish, were brought in increasing quantities by canal. Indeed, Cheshire supplies to Manchester were to be unloaded at a special Potato Wharf adjoining the Castlefield basin.

In hard times there was little else save potatoes and skimmed milk, called blue milk. There were periods when the children gathered sour docks and nettles, which were cooked with the oatmeal. Indeed, when the grain harvests failed during the closing years of the eighteenth century and again in 1812, suffering was so severe that food riots broke out in several of the manufacturing areas.

From the second decade of the nineteenth century hand-loom weavers were hard pressed to make a living. There was little left for emergencies. William Varley, of Higham, near Burnley, noted in his diary in the winter of 1822 his attempt to arrest consumption in one of his children. He bought a few quarts of new milk, some ling liver oil (equivalent to cod-liver oil) and a mustard plaster. It was of no avail, and her death was recorded under the date 8 January 1823. Four years later in the New Year of 1827 he wrote, 'Sickness and disease also prevails very much and well it may, the clamming and starving and hard working which the poor are now undergoing, it is no wonder if it should bring death itself.' Again a month later he noted children dying 'by two and three a house' of smallpox and measles. He added, '. . . well may they die, for there is no aid, no succour to be had for them'.[7] Varley with his garden and hens was perhaps a little better off than some. Even so, he came near to despair.

In town and country the record is of increasing poverty among hand-loom cotton weavers. In Manchester even the most frugal worker could provide little except bread, meal and potatoes for his family. The penny-a-week burial subscription was met with difficulty.[8] The most detailed records of distress, however, come from the village of Marsden, where the local Quakeress, Ann Ecroyd, provided relief during times of hardship over the twenty years between 1824 and 1843. In the acute periods of privation, when earnings amounted to no more than two pence a week per head, she distributed boiled rice, seasoned with allspice and salt and rationed at a pint a head daily. She described how, during the worst depressions, families sold their furniture and shared houses. Often the only clothes on the bed were rice bags or a single patched blanket. Fever carried off many of the children.[9]

Quaker relief extended to neighbouring areas, and again there were meticulous records. One hand-loom weaver was said to have kept his large family alive on the potatoes he grew which they ate three times as day.[10] Another with a family of six, whose wife had never recovered from her last confinement, had received meal and 6s 6d from the parish, but the sum barely covered the debt owed to the doctor.

In their recollections domestic workers' children described the affection of the home, their enjoyment of simple wholesome food and the warmth of relationships within many of the small communities. In times of illness they were dosed with homely remedies, perhaps exceptionally with the brew recommended by the diarist, John Rowbottom of Oldham, 'for colds and coughs which have almost settled into consumption', a mixture of linseed, liquorice, brown sugar, rum and white vinegar.[11] However, there were less pleasant doses which perhaps they did not remember, including the sleeping cordials (the most common known as 'Godfrey's') which were widely used to keep infants quiet during daily work. A former druggist's apprentice in a hand-loom district recalled that his 'master used to make Godfrey in a large boiler by twenties and thirties of gallons at a brewst'.[12]

Of the '20s and later years children had searing memories of wretchedness and destitution. They themselves heard stories of their parents' sufferings in the former 'barley times'. At the worst their own food was little but thin gruel and their clothing barely more than sacking.[13] Frequently adults clung to domestic industry to keep the family together as a working unit and maintain control of their children. Even when faced with the relentless competition of the power-driven machinery, they struggled to retain the traditional way of life. In the long term, however, despite the threat to the family and to parental authority, the pressures were irresistible. Sometimes whole families sought employment in factories; in other cases, men who found too painful the prospect of a discipline 'tee'd to a bell' sent their children, and their wives, to the mills.

It was from the moorland cottages, smallholdings and hamlets, as well as from farther afield, that people were drawn into the growing mill towns and villages. Existing towns grew in size. In Lancashire Preston, already in 1780 a place of some distinction with a population of 6,000, grew to 33,000 by 1831. Bolton in a similar period increased from 5,000 to 43,000, Oldham from 12,000 to 51,000, Ashton under Lyne from 5,000 to 34,000. In Cheshire the traditional silk button-making towns of Macclesfield and Congleton grew as the industry expanded to include the production of silk yarns and fabrics and to include cotton manufacture. The fastest growth, however, came in

Stockport—a town of 50,000 by 1831—where cotton took over from silk, and in the new cotton areas of Dukinfield, Stalybridge and Hyde. Hyde, for example, increased in population almost tenfold between 1801 and 1831 to over 7,000. Even more dramatic was the expansion in neighbouring Stalybridge, where between 1755 and 1825, no more than a single lifetime, the population grew from 140 to 12,000.[14]

Of the new mechanisation processes spinning came first, followed, after a temporary boom in hand-loom weaving, by the power-driven factory looms. In some of the Pennine valleys the traditional woollen manufacture continued alongside the cotton industry. Elsewhere, as in Manchester, Salford and Eccles, there were silk factories, though the scale of the trade was dwarfed by the growth of cotton.

Already before the end of the eighteenth century the centre of the industrial society was Manchester, described as 'the heart of this vast system, the circulating branches of which spread all around it . . .'.[15] During the following century it was to become the great 'cottonopolis' of the country, a finishing and trading centre which commercially and politically represented the interests of a wider area. Even by the turn of the century the introduction of steam-power had precipitated its growth as a factory town, and within two to three decades it was the major centre of both spinning and weaving. It was of the Ancoats district that Engels wrote in 1843 when he described 'the largest mills . . . lining the canals, colossal six and seven-storied buildings towering with their slender chimneys far above the low cottages of the workers'.[16] Outlying areas, including Hulme, Chorlton and Ardwick, were similarly industrialised and continued as important manufacturing centres through the greater part of the century.

It was the textile industry that gave the towns their unmistakable character. However, the proportion employed in textiles varied from area to area and, within areas, so also did the proportions employed in the different processes—spinning, weaving, bleaching, dyeing and printing. Everywhere the number of textile workers were swollen by employees in ancillary trades, in coal mines, ironworks, foundries and sawmills, as well as casual labourers and a host of retailers, shopkeepers, beer-house keepers, publicans and the like. The scale of the cotton industry became immense. Prophetically in the mid-nineteenth century an observer had remarked of the Lancashire towns that 'good times . . . hang on the fibre of cotton . . .'.[17] A few years later at the time of the cotton famine it was estimated that out of a national population of twenty million, over two million, including members of families, were cut off from their source of support. Half were directly dependent on cotton and half on allied trades. At the same period silk towns, like Macclesfield with 40,000 people, had reached peak populations.

Families were of widely different strata, depending on the skill and character of the main wage-earner; the obvious gradations were between the skilled, semi-skilled, unskilled and casual workers but within categories there were often fine distinctions. However, setbacks, whether self-inflicted or otherwise, could quickly change fortunes and bring artisans' offspring to the level of those of the lowest workers. Families were brought down by drink, by illness and above all by trade fluctuation. Every decade brought one or more periods of depression, sometimes brief but at other times so protracted and intense that they threatened to overwhelm households. At such times many wage-earners were reduced to a state of utter dejection and their families were listless with hunger and despair. There were few adults in the area at any point in the nineteenth century who had not experienced periods of real poverty. Their outlook and attitude to their own children, therefore, reflected their own fears, insecurity and uncertainty.

'Whoever says the Industrial Revolution says cotton.'[18] It was the application of steam power to machinery that transformed the location of the early cotton factories. The first spinning mills were driven by water power from the swift-flowing Pennine streams. In the remote areas labour was scarce and many employers imported child apprentices, parish orphans from workhouses far and near. Clearly, overseers of the poor were only too keen to get rid of the orphans. One London parish dispatched an idiot with every twenty sound children.[19] At worst, children were brought like 'cartloads of live lumber' and abandoned to their fate. Feargus O'Connor recalled, in a speech in Oldham in 1836, that a former guard of the London and Manchester coach had told him that 'scores of poor children, taken from workhouses or kidnapped in the streets of the metropolis, used to be brought down by that coach to Manchester and slid into a cellar in Mosley Street as if they had been stones or any other inanimate substance'.[20]

There were advertisements of orphan children in the local papers when overseers typically offered 'a Number of healthy Boys and Girls ... as apprentices'. However, because workhouse children were often weak, ill fed and prone to infection, individual manufacturers were discriminating and took care to lay down terms. At Helmshore mill in Rossendale, workhouse children from Hertfordshire were only accepted if they were accompanied by a man and wife; the former was

Quarry Bank Mill, Styal, built by Samuel Greg in 1784. Note the rural situation

to find his own employment while the latter was to look after 'the children's comforts and morals'. They were, moreover, to be sent with sufficient clothing, beds and bedding.[21]

At Quarry Bank, Styal, Samuel Greg, in response to offers of orphan apprentices from Staffordshire and elsewhere, was careful in his selection. Girls were usually preferred to boys, but in either case only children who passed examination by his physician were taken. Overall some two-thirds were judged to be healthy. A number who were obviously enfeebled, as well as the occasional child who was 'weak in the intellect' or 'dwarfish', were excluded. Others were accepted on probation for up to a year to see if they proved sufficiently robust. For those selected extra clothing and a premium of two guineas were required. Once at Styal they were boarded in a special apprentice house and fed on wholesome food. On arrival they were vaccinated by Greg's physician, sometimes twenty or thirty at a time. Indeed, oversight and treatment of the children by the physician, who visited weekly in winter and monthly in summer, has been described as 'the earliest example of an industrial medical service in England'.[22]

Though labour was long, and especially tedious by candlelight during the winter months, there were periods of relief when power was less brisk and apprentices were allowed intervals of play outside. At a whistle from the spinners they returned to work. The abandonment of candles at springtime was a cause of general rejoicing. The factory cash book records on 31 March 1792 the gift of £1 11s 6d to the 'girles' for a dance. Presumably the boys shared in the £2 10s given for the men's drink.[23]

So great was the demand for child labour that employers had agents scouring the countryside to recruit children from parents themselves. Among the Styal records are contracts between Greg and parents in other areas.[24] In return for board and lodging and a wage of about ninepence a week children were 'bound' until the age of twenty-one. Under certain contracts they were to be released for one week in every year in order to return home. Other employers, like Samuel Oldknow of Mellor, found jobs for fathers outside their factories in order to attract families to the area so that they could draw on child and female labour.[25] Indeed, as the Gregs found, the cost of keeping apprentices rose so steeply (by the 1820s the average per child was 5s a week, and twenty years later, more than double again)[26] that the

N.º 24

Be it remembered, it is this Day agreed by
and between SAMUEL GREG, of *Styal*, in the County of *Chester*, of the one Part, and *Peter and Sarah Stockton*
———————————————————————— of
Keel in the County of Stafford —— of the other Part,
as follows: That the said *Sarah Stockton* —— shall
serve the said SAMUEL GREG, in his Cotton-Mills, in *Styal*, in the
County of *Chester*, as a just and honest Servant, *Twelve*
Hours in each of the six working Days, and to be at *her* own
Liberty at all other Times; the Commencement of the Hours
to be fixed from Time to Time by the said SAMUEL GREG, for
the Term of *Eight* Year*s* at the Wages of *Nine Pence*
p Week the first Year and One Shilling p Week
the Remaining part of the Term and Mr Greg
Engages to find the Said Sarah Stockton with meats
Drink, Washing and Lodging For the Above Term
Sufficient for One in her Station ————
And that if the said *Sarah Stockton* ——————
shall absent *herself* from the Service of the said SAMUEL GREG,
in the said working Hours, during the said Term, without
his Consent first obtained, that the said SAMUEL GREG, may
abate the Wages in a double Proportion for such Absence; and
the said SAMUEL GREG shall be at Liberty, during the Term, to
discharge the Servant from his Service, for Misbehaviour, or
Want of Employ.

As WITNESS their Hands, this —— *Tenth* —— Day of
October —— 179*6*

Witness   *Sarah Stockton his Mark*
Matt Faulkner   *Peter Stockton his Mark* ✕

Sarah Stockton is to be allowed One week in Every
Year to go See her Friends ————

Agreement between Samuel Greg and the parents of a Staffordshire girl who entered
his service

whole system became uneconomic.

In contrast to benevolent employers there were others who treated their children, particularly parish orphans, as slaves. Time lost by lack of water was made up by excessive overtime, and children in the low-built water frames were deformed for life. John Moss, former master of apprentices at the remote Backbarrow Mill, described in 1816 the condition of his charges, some 150 children taken from London and Liverpool workhouses at the age of seven upwards. From Monday to Saturday they worked fourteen hours a day, and on Sunday were compelled, in defiance of the law, to clean machinery from 6 a.m. to noon. Some children, he said, had fallen asleep after their work and had to be carried to the apprentice house at night. He alleged that in times of slack trade apprentices had been turned adrift to fend for themselves. He himself had preferred to take a less well paid post as master of Preston workhouse rather than stay at Backbarrow Mill.[27]

Large-scale employers advertised their need both to dispose of and to engage child labour. For example, Wheeler's *Manchester Chronicle* of 7 August 1784 contained the following: 'To let, the Labour of 260 Children with Rooms and every Convenience for carrying on the Cotton Business ... '.[28] Again typical of the many advertisements under the heading 'Wanted' in the *Manchester Mercury* was 'A Mill with a constant and regular supply of water near a town or village where a number of children may be had on easy terms'. In the same issue of 6 February 1787 a Clitheroe employer announced that he 'Wanted Immediately ... Children who perfectly understand spinning Cotton Twist'.

There were orphan children who were worked in shifts night and day. As one batch replaced another, the beds were seldom cold. Less is known of the smaller factories which took a few parish children to supplement their free labour. Often, because their margins were fine, they oppressed children by overwork. In one case in the Rossendale valley the upper rooms where apprentices were housed were so ramshackle that they collapsed.[29]

With the introduction of steam engines factories could be located in areas where plenty of free labour was available. Manchester, where the first steam-driven mill was built by Arkwright in 1780, had over fifty such factories by 1800. The functional five or six-storeyed buildings, usually gas-lit from the early years of the nineteenth century, imposed a discipline of mechanisation. 'There is no idleness among us,' said one of the Manchester managers to Robert Southey, 'The wheels never stand still.'[30] Hours were inflexible. 'They must attend like clockwork,' reported a Stockport manufacturer at the inquiry of 1816.[31] Indeed, it was 'the strict and almost superstitious discipline' of the large factories that impressed visitors. Employers likened the control required to that of a regiment or a ship.[32] Always they insisted—as they continued to do in future years—that children must start at an early age while their fingers were nimble or they would never become skilled workers.

Other mills, in contrast, were run by small employers who had bought 'room and power'. As in Oldham, many were in makeshift premises, simply cottages joined together, to which a steam engine had been attached.[33] Here were some of the worst working conditions. There was no gas lighting in such small-scale works; even large factories like that at Quarry Bank did not install gas until the 1860s.

Though at the 1816 inquiry manufacturers evaded questions on children's age ('We have always endeavoured to get the largest children we could; they are the most profitable,' said one), it was clear that there were many children of seven and eight working from 6 a.m. to 8 p.m.[34] Even so, these little bobbin doffers, piecers and scavengers in the spinning mills were thought to be better off than some of the children who lived and worked in the underground cellars which served as hand weavers' shops and who at nine years and upwards were weaving fine cottons.

Like many children Samuel Bamford was brought to live in Manchester at the end of the eighteenth century. He recalled that, as he and his father approached on their journey from the village of Middleton, there was

... a vast gloom darkening before us ... Then we heard the rumbling of wheels, and the clang of hammers, and a hubbub of confused sounds from workshops and manufactories, ... on the top of Red Bank, the glare of many lights and faint outlines of buildings in a noisy chaos below told us we beheld Manchester.[35]

The river Irk, in whose clear water Middleton children had paddled and where trout had been caught, was here transformed into inky darkness. Unlike the majority of newcomers Bamford within a few years returned, to his intense joy, to his birthplace. Most stayed in

Manchester or whatever town they had gone to, and were often joined by kin or by former neighbours and friends.

The abundance of work for children was an incentive to have large families. As Thomas Henry, the Manchester apothecary, wrote in 1790, 'Every child that is born may be regarded as an addition to fortune.'[36] In the early factories the family unit was in some measure retained. Particularly in the outlying areas the cotton spinner employed his own children, who started as scavengers cleaning the machinery and sweeping the cotton waste and later became piecers joining the broken threads. In the towns, where fathers came as unskilled in-migrants,[37] there was less opportunity to keep working links.[38] Rather children were hired out to spinners; in the words of a commentator, they were 'let out ... upon the same principle as a postmaster lets out post horses'.[39] In fact the severity of discipline was in part a consequence of the high mobility of labour; so many employees, adults and children alike, were transient and changed jobs with great frequency.

Factory children were able to make a significant contribution to family income. Though wages fluctuated, it has been calculated that between 1810 and 1819 children of ten in Manchester earned between 2s 6d and 3s a week and those of fourteen about 7s 6d.[40] Even in a skilled worker's family two children at these ages might be contributing a quarter of the total income; in a hand-loom weaver's household children of similar ages might be earning about as much as their father at the earlier date and much more than him by 1819.[41] Without going to the factory, girls of nine could earn 2s 'nursing for a neighbour', that is, looking after the infant of a working mother. Younger children made themselves useful and, particularly where homes were at a distance from work, carried meals to the factory once and sometimes twice a day.

In 1819 40 per cent of the labour force in one of Manchester's largest mills, McConnel and Kennedy's, were aged between eight and fifteen.[42] It was one of the firm's spinners who two years later wrote ecstatically of Manchester:

> Hail splendid scene! The Nurse of every art,
> That glads the widow's and the orphan's heart!
> Thy Mills, like gorgeous palaces, arise,
> And lift their useful turrets to the skies![43]

Contemporary domestic workers might have expressed different feelings. Nor were the wages their children earned uniformly high. In outlying areas rates were much lower. It was a measure of the desperate circumstances in such areas in the late '20s that, for the sake of a shilling a week, offspring were sent to the factory at the age of five, children who had to be carried to work and who, once there, had to be terrorised to stay awake.[44]

With their concentration of workers in hot, humid rooms many factories were breeding grounds for disease. It was in 1784 that public attention was drawn to the effect on children's health of the factory regime by a group of Manchester doctors, including Thomas Percival, now Physician Extraordinary at the Manchester Infirmary. The occurrence was an outbreak of 'low putrid fever', in fact typhus, in cotton mills at Radcliffe, near Bury.[45] The report of the doctors listed causes of aggravation including the close factory atmosphere, dominated by the offensive smells of rancid machine oil, and the overtaxing of children by long hours of confinement. As a temporary measure they advocated weekly fumigation of workrooms by tobacco and the smoking of tobacco by those, including 'superintendents of the works', who were exposed to infection. Their long term recommendations emphasised the need of ventilation, disinfecting and whitewashing of factories and of 'strict observance of cleanliness . . . on all who work in the mills'.

They made special reference to child workers and to the need to reduce their hours of labour, on the grounds that 'active recreation of children and youth are necessary to growth, vigour and the right conformation of the body'. Their suggestions extended to the provision of schooling so that '. . . the rising generation should not be debarred from all opportunities of instruction at the only season of life in which they can be properly improved'. Concern roused by this and similar outbreaks of the 'Alarming Sickness' was such that county justices refused to allow apprentices to be bound in factories where they would be worked at night.

II CHILDREN AND THE ENVIRONMENT

Health hazards were aggravated by the increasing size of urban populations and by the numbers of people on the move who brought disease with them. In the older towns there were many cellar dwellings with ceilings only a few inches above street level. Manchester's damp and unflagged cellars were described as 'graves of the living . . . holes where the light of the sun never reaches and where pure and wholesome air is not admitted'.[1] Here, as in neighbouring towns like Preston and Stockport, cellars were used as hand-loom weaving shops or taken as dwellings by newcomers.

In the smaller industrial communities families had the benefit of fresh air and country surroundings. In exceptional factory 'colonies' like Thomas Ashton's at Flowery Field, Hyde, homes were altogether superior, with a separate kitchen, pantry and two or more bedrooms. Often, however, there was little to choose between the houses—'one up and one down', with a fireplace as the sole amenity—that were hastily flung up by factory owners in outlying areas and those in congested urban streets. It was the general conditions of life that were very different.

In the villages food was cheaper. Milk was readily available and bought in quantity; mostly it was skimmed milk at a penny a quart which was sold as well as buttermilk at half the price (new milk at 'tuppence' a quart was for the better-off). Most of the earnings went on food, of which the staple items were oatmeal, flour and potatoes. Oatmeal porridge sweetened with treacle was a filling food, especially for children, and, depending on the district and the price of flour, oatcakes, bread or hard dough cakes, made with 'ordinary' as distinct from 'best' flour, were eaten with broth.[2] In times of high prices families grew their own potatoes and vegetables. Meat, bacon, cheese and butter, bought in small amounts, had to go a long way. Rare treats, as a former factory child remembered, were sweet tea and toasted cake, or a quart of peas or mussels and cockles shared among the family.[3]

In stark contrast were conditions in Manchester, which by the first census in 1801 had a population of 70,000. It was one thing in a semi-rural area to fetch water from the river and to fling refuse to the winds but quite another for dwellers in the congested streets and crowded courts and alleys. The temptation was to sink to the level of the most feckless. For the women, as Frances Collier pointed out, factory work was a refuge from homes so wretched that even the bravest efforts achieved little.[4]

It was in the subterranean vaults of Manchester that whole families succumbed to typhus fever, which broke out in virulent form in 1789 and again seven years later. In the emergency of 1796 a Board of Health was established by local medical men, including Thomas Percival and his colleague on the Infirmary staff, John Ferriar, in an endeavour to control the epidemic. The latter, who as Infirmary physician visited the sick poor in their homes, described child fever victims. He referred to 'a boy of seven whose body was distended and [whose] tongue [was] covered with a thick brown crust. His countenance was ghastly and clay coloured.'[5] On many occasions in the hottest weather he found several members of a family lying ill together in hovels, 'where the dead remained for whole days by the side of the survivors, and where delirium and insensibility were states to be envied'.[6] Sometimes only rags lay between the sick and the damp earth beneath, and so dark were the cellar interiors that even during daytime he had to examine patients by candlelight. He blamed mothers who kept children in dirty clothes and who, instead of the 'hard labour' of washing, worked daily in the cotton mills.[7]

In the factories the people themselves, like the floors and machinery, were 'filthy beyond belief'. By night the smell of candles poisoned the atmosphere. Ferriar stressed the harmful effect of night work on children, since it deprived them 'of fresh air and exercise which nature points out as essential in childhood and youth'.[8] The violent change of temperature as they emerged from the heat of the factory into the sharp morning air affected their lungs. Immediately on their return home they threw themselves into the one family bed, still warm from the bodies which had just left it.

In 1796 the Board of Health established in Portland Street a fever hospital, encouragingly named the House of Recovery. Here patients were carried by sedan chair and treated by immersion in cold water; in the worst cases opium was administered. Later rebuilt in Aytoun Street, the hospital was furnished with iron bedsteads without hangings and with straw mattresses which were changed frequently. It was fumigated with nitre and vitriolic acid twice daily, and the bodies of the dead were wrapped in pitched cloth. Meanwhile patients' homes were lime-washed in order to reduce the infection. The Board of Health appealed for support on the grounds that the fever wards preserved breadwinners and therefore decreased the number of orphans dependent on the public purse.[9] Small fever hospitals were established in Stockport and Preston, though no provision was made in other neighbouring areas where the fever raged.

The Board of Health advised families to take precautions so that children might avoid contagion. They should be fed and washed before they went to work, and on their return they should not be allowed to sleep in working clothes or get into unmade beds. Instead of 'just tea with little nourishment' they should be given regular meals of rice and soup. As for clothing, flannel next to the skin would 'counteract . . . the bad effects of cold and dampness and would prevent many fevers and rheumatic infections'.[10] Against overcrowding families themselves could do little. Conditions were such that the healthy were compelled to live constantly in the atmosphere of the sick.

The Board's exposure of the effects of overwork on factory children was given wide publicity. It warned against a system which 'tends to diminish future expectations as to the general sum of life and industry by impairing strength and destroying the stamina of the rising generation'.[11] Already in 1784, following his investigations at Radcliffe, Percival had taken a stand against the night work of parish apprentices. Before the Manchester Board of Health he called attention to conditions of employment in factories and proposed the need for legislation for 'the wise, humane and *equal* government of all such works'. As president of the fever hospital Sir Robert Peel drew on the evidence of the Manchester doctors in support of his legislation in 1802 to protect apprentice children in cotton mills from abuses of overwork.[12] Though restricted in scope, the measure was to be the beginning of a new code of regulation which extended to all child workers in textile factories.

Meanwhile the House of Recovery was expanding its range of treatment. Smallpox cases were admitted to a separate ward. The new building was designed to isolate infections. Thus in 1805 an outbreak of scarlet fever among children was effectively suppressed by isolation, a relatively novel practice at the time.

It was in 1832, some thirty years after the major outbreaks of fever which had led to the establishment of the Manchester Board of Health, that the approach of cholera inspired similar fear and alarm. The increasingly dense populations in narrow unsewered streets were a fertile source of contagion. In fact in Manchester, as elsewhere in the region, outbreaks could usually be traced to crowded lodging houses used by people on the move. Children were among the earliest victims, particularly in the Manchester district of 'Little Ireland', described by Gaulter, the cholera historian, as 'a damp and dismal sort of excavation on the banks of the Medlock'.[13] Many of the children were half starving and in rags. Several had eaten a red herring for their last meal or rotten fruit picked up in Shude Hill market or, in sheer hunger, they had gnawed a raw potato.

Children stood a better chance of recovery than older patients. However, relatively few of those affected were employed in the factories, which now, some thirty years after Ferriar's time, were large, spacious and healthy compared with the squalid homes in damp, crowded courts reeking from the stench of cesspools and dunghills. Just how important cleanliness was in keeping disease at bay was seen at the Stockport Sunday school where scholars were required as a condition of entrance to come clean. Out of the total of 5,000 members not one fell victim of the disease.[14]

Perhaps the main effect of the cholera was the feeling of terror the outbreaks roused. Towns were encouraged to make preparations. On the instruction of Whitehall special precautions were taken in Manchester and other towns in the area; empty premises were equipped as cholera hospitals and there were hasty arrangements for scavenging and for the clearance of urban pigstyes. By public notices people were urged to take precautions by regularly washing themselves all over with salt and water and by frequently limewashing and fumigating their homes.

In Manchester there was popular horror associated with the high death rate of the cholera hospital and with the sight of the cholera van 'rattling . . . through the streets . . . the dead carts followed by the mourner or two at an awful distance'. [15] There was also, despite the fear of infection, suffering and resentment as a consequence of the seizure and burning of clothes and bedding.[16] There were dark crimes long recollected of the cholera hospitals. In particular, there was an incident following the gruesome discovery by an old man of the headless trunk of his grandchild, John Brogan, who had died in the Swan Street hospital. The havoc which followed, including mob attack during which the head was recovered and transferred, together with the body, for safe keeping in the town hall, subsided only when troops of the 15th Hussars were called in. On enquiry it transpired that the newly appointed hospital dispenser had severed the head and replaced it with a brick covered in shavings.[17] Such an occurence inflamed popular imagination and strengthened hostility not only against hospitals but against members of the medical profession who, for purposes of dissection, were suspected of encouraging murder.

III CHILD MORTALITY AND DISEASE

In the pre-industrial period high infant and child mortality rates had been taken for granted. In the towns, particularly, children had been vulnerable to conditions of overcrowding and dirt. The growing textile areas were now similarly fatal. In 1789 Percival contrasted the child death rate in Manchester with that of the neighbouring country township of Royton.[1] Half those born in Manchester died before the age of five (most of them before the age of three), compared with one in seven before the age of three in Royton. A recent (1968) analysis of the burial registers of the chapelry of Colne at a similar period confirms the better chance of survival of children in the smaller communities, particularly where, as in Colne and the neighbouring villages, the area was elevated and well drained. Of infants baptised in the chapelry in 1801, again the proportion who died under the age of three was one in seven.[2]

As elsewhere, the causes of death in the parish bills of mortality are vague. The term 'fever', for example, was used indiscriminately to cover a great range of infection which had not been differentiated, and even distinctions between 'low fever', 'intermittent fever' and 'factory fever' are scarcely meaningful. In fact typhus fever, which scourged the area periodically, cut down adolescents and adults rather than children. Indirectly, however, children suffered; because of the loss of breadwinners they were left to survive as best they could. Enfeebled by poverty, they themselves fell early prey to disease, to one of the child infections or to smallpox.

For infants even more than adults the recorded causes of death may well have been only the final symptom or even a convenient category. Such terms as 'weakness', 'convulsions', 'fits', 'teething' could cover a multitude of conditions brought on by drugging and misfeeding. Similarly, 'debility', 'infant decline' and 'consumption' referred to those who withered away. Even so, something can be gleaned from the lists of fatalities of young children. There were, of course, innumerable fevers—worm fever, rash fever, tooth fever, brain fever and scarlet fever—as well as throat diseases, croup and thrush (known colloquially as 'frog'), and 'water on the brain' (later diagnosed as tuberculous meningitis).

Numbers of infants died at birth or very soon afterwards. Indeed, according to current theory, male foetuses because of their size were more at risk. Not only did they need more nourishment than those of females during gestation, but they were in greater danger at birth.[3] There were also still-births, perhaps ten per cent of total births according to some burial registers, and other still-born infants who were quietly disposed of. Infanticide, too, frequently escaped detection.

Many infants survived only briefly. Weaklings with their fragile hold on life succumbed early in urban conditions, where malnutrition and dirt were the underlying causes of death. Thereafter, from the age of five to ten, death rates between manufacturing towns and country districts varied less. In the words of the Manchester surgeon, John Roberton, 'the reason is that in the former most of the sickly and feeble die in the first year of life. Consequently only the vigorous, in general, attain their fifth year and above.'[4]

Among infections smallpox had scourged the child population in the past. Percival calculated that, between 1754 and 1774, one in nine of those whose births were registered at the Manchester Collegiate Church died of smallpox, three-fifths of them between the ages of six months and two years.[5] Many were the offspring of poor families whose uncleanliness aggravated the disease. He stressed, however, that the incidence of teething increased the danger and accordingly was in favour of the inoculation of healthy infants (by the method known as variolation) at the age of two months. In the treatment of smallpox itself he quoted the success of the 'cool regimen' pursued by 'an ingenious apothecary' in Manchester who had attended in a single year seventy patients, most of them very young children, of whom only two had died.[6] His own prescription for the secondary fever was a warm bath, 'prepared of a decoction of chamomile leaves and flowers, with a proper quantity of buttermilk added to it . . . It cleans the skin of putrid sores . . ., softens the postules, opens the pores, promotes perspiration . . .'.[7] Such treatment assumed a level of care which exceeded the capacity of many households.

It frequently happened that, at the same time as typhus fever cut down adults, smallpox struck the infant population. Such was the case in the '80s and '90s in Manchester. With monotonous regularity the burial registers of churches such as St John's, Deansgate, listed deaths from smallpox of infants from seven weeks upwards. On typical pages two-thirds or even four-fifths of all recorded deaths were of infants; of infants and children together, five-sixths of deaths were attributed to smallpox. During the worst of the typhus and smallpox epidemics,

Extract from the 1793 burial register of St John's Church, Deansgate, Manchester. Note the variety of parental occupations, including 'Horse-miliner', or harness-maker

JAMES FILDES,

CABINET and COFFIN MAKER,

At No. 66, *Shude-hill*, MANCHESTER,

Takes this Method to inform his FRIENDS and the PUBLIC,

That from the repeated Applications for

Coffins ready made,

Has induced him to inform the PUBLIC,

That in future he will have Coffins of all Sizes ready

made, both for Children and aged Perſons.

Any FAMILY that may be in want of the ſame,

May be ſerved on the loweſt Terms,

And will have to wait no longer than the Name

and Age can be wrote on the Plate.

N. B. *The above will not be ſold on the* Sabbath **Day,**

as they may be had at ſo ſhort Notice.

JULY 25, 1795.

RADFORD AND SIMPSON, PRINTERS.

Handbill advertisement for coffins in Manchester, 1795

coffins of all sizes were made in advance and were available on demand.

Periodically measles were fatal to numbers of two- and three-year-olds, though the death rate was relatively low compared with that from smallpox. Unlike smallpox, however, it was particularly fatal to males. Percival described the violence of the accompanying symptoms of inflammation of the lungs and also the treatment—cutting of the vein, blistering and dosing with 'seneka' root.[8] Of epidemics in general contemporaries had noted that their severity was related to dry seasons. Percival's deductions were more specific: he calculated that the worst years were those when early summer rains were followed by prolonged hot spells. At that point vapours from the damp low-lying land became 'constant, copious and often putrid'.[9]

By the turn of the century the declining virulence of smallpox and the use of both inoculation and the new vaccination helped to reduce the high level of deaths. Even so, it was still considerable. Examination of the records of the Nonconformist New Windsor Chapel, Salford, whose members came from a fair cross-section of occupations, shows that between 1800 and 1802 one-fifth of children buried under the age of ten died of smallpox, most of them between the ages of one and five.[10]

Gradually, however, during the early years of the nineteenth century other infections began to take a greater toll than smallpox—whooping cough, known as chin-cough or chink-cough, with infants and measles with young children. From the registers of the Rusholme cemetery, Manchester, which covered factory areas including Ardwick, Hulme and Chorlton, John Roberton found that over the four-year period 1821–25 measles was twice as fatal to young children as smallpox. It had now become 'a serious and dangerous disease'.[11] In 1830 the fever hospital sought to contain an outbreak by setting aside a ward for measles but the infection was on too great a scale for isolation to be effective.

Smallpox, however, continued to be a dreaded disease which periodically struck down children who had not been vaccinated. From his calculations in 1826 Roberton found it ranked after 'infantile decline', 'convulsions' and measles as a major cause of death.[12] Five years previously the bill of mortality in Blackburn had shown it as the

Macclesfield Sunday School. The building, opened in 1814 and catering for some 2,500 children, is probably the largest of the early Sunday Schools to survive in the area

single largest cause of child deaths.[13] Everywhere those who recovered were scarred for life; in Macauley's words, the disease left 'hideous traces of its power, turning the babe into a changeling at which the mother shuddered'.

Among factory children themselves many suffered from scrofula, incipient consumption visible by the enlarged neck glands and white swellings of the joints. At best children who survived into adolescence outgrew the disease, though the deformities themselves persisted; in some cases, however, limbs had to be amputated and at worst children worked until they died.[14] Consumption was also attributed to inflammation of the chest, the result of sudden changes of temperature of up to 40° in transition from the hot atmosphere of the mill to the cold of the street outside.[15] According to evidence from Stockport in 1819, 200 children had died within a year of consumption.[16] The death rate, however, was only part of the picture; the other was the general deterioration of the population.

IV FAMILY SELF-HELP

Most families had to cope themselves with crises of sickness, birth and death. There were often relatives under the same roof or nearby who helped, or a neighbour could be called in. A local woman, like 'Owd Jacky Wife' who came to Ben Brierley's mother in childbirth in Failsworth, usually obliged as midwife.[1] There were occasions when, through misjudgement or reluctance to take time off, the working wife gave birth unexpectedly. As Stella Davies records, her great-grandmother was too shy to ask the mill overlooker and 'left it too late'.[2] In the coalfields, similarly, women were known to have brought up the pit shafts their newly born infants.[3]

At the other extreme there were available, for those who could afford a guinea or more, accoucheurs. In Manchester, for example, Richard Hall, honorary surgeon to the Infirmary, attended some 4,000 lying-in cases.[4] Another member of the staff of the Infirmary, Charles White (later one of the founders of the Manchester Lying-in Hospital) had gained his early experience as midwife among the parish poor. He described the conditions which brought on puerperal fever. Customarily the woman in labour was in a hot room, surrounded by her friends. After the birth she was kept in bed till the ninth day with the window shut, curtains drawn round her bed and a fire burning.[5] They were the very antithesis of the conditions he recommended in his book on midwifery. 'The lying-in chamber is to be in every respect . . . sweet and clean . . . The room is to be brushed every day . . . the patient is to be often supplied with clean linen and clean well-aired sheets are to be laid upon the bed . . .'. His insistence that the patient should sit up in bed on the second day and by the fourth should get out of bed was quite novel.[6]

Childbirth was perilous. Some of the death rates recorded in bills of mortality were startlingly high. Blackburn lists in 1810 recorded fourteen such deaths out of a total of thirty-seven deaths of females aged between fifteen and forty; ten years later there were ten childbed deaths out of a total of fifty-nine female deaths.[7]

Even among women attended by skilled midwives the death rate could be high where standards of personal cleanliness were neglected. Any inkling that apparently clean hands could carry infection lay far in the future. White himself commented on two male midwives in the

The Yearly Bill of
MORTALITY
For the Parish Church and Town of Blackburn,
From DECEMBER 21, 1809, to DECEMBER 21, 1810.

	CHRISTENINGS.			BURIALS.				MARRIED
	Males.	Fem's.	Total.	Males.	Fem's.	Aborts	Total.	Marriages.
PARISH CHURCH,	278	294	572	177	206	48	431	307
SAINT JOHN'S...	10	18	28	12	19	1	32	0
SAINT PAUL'S....	113	111	224	26	27	4	57	0
INDEPENDENTS .	15	14	29	15	17	4	36	0
METHODISTS.....	11	11	22	0	0	0	0	0
BAPTISTS	4	6	10	3	4	0	7	0
CATHOLICS......	19	15	34	0	0	0	0	0
TOTAL........	450	469	919	233	273	57	563	307

Monthly Report for the Parish Church.

	CHRISTENED.			BURIED.				MARRIED.	
	Males.	Fem's.	Total.	Males.	Fem's.	Aborts	Total.	Licen.	Bans.
DECEMBER	15	11	26	8	4	1	13	1	10
JANUARY	19	19	38	15	20	6	41	3	28
FEBRUARY	16	18	34	17	17	3	37	1	27
MARCH	21	17	38	21	16	7	43	4	29
APRIL............	38	41	79	13	27	8	48	6	27
MAY.............	22	25	47	22	25	2	49	2	23
JUNE	22	24	46	13	18	2	33	3	18
JULY	30	22	52	18	15	4	37	1	23
AUGUST	27	30	57	7	11	4	22	1	13
SEPTEMBER.....	19	35	54	10	10	2	22	4	20
OCTOBER........	22	26	48	13	16	4	33	2	26
NOVEMBER.....,	18	17	35	11	20	2	33	1	27
DECEMBER	9	9	18	9	8	3	20	0	7
TOTAL	278	294	572	177	206	48	431	29	278

DISEASES.	Males.	Fem's.
Consumptions, ...	34	54
Fits, ...	34	30
Fever, ...	19	17
Old age, ...	21	37
Dropsy, ...	6	2
Child-bed, ...	0	14
Small pox, ...	6	9
Measles, ...	0	3
Hooping cough, ...	7	11
Teeth, ...	3	3
Worm fever, ...	6	7
Palsy, ...	3	1
Inflammation, ...	8	7
Asthma, ...	4	1
Gravel, ...	1	0
Appoplexy, ...	0	2
Rheumatism, ...	1	0
Fistula, ...	1	0
Decayed liver, ...	1	0
Rupture, ...	0	1
Croup, ...	6	0
Water in the head, ..	5	1
Pleurisy, ...	1	0
White swelling, ...	0	1
Mortification, ...	1	0
Cancer, ...	1	0
Scurvy, ...	0	1
CASUALTIES.		
Burnt, ...	1	1
Scalded, ...	0	2
Killed by falling, ..	2	0
Drowned, ...	2	0
Bursting blood vessel,	1	0
Killed by a cart, ..	0	1
Killed in a quarrel, ..	1	0
Excess of drinking,...	1	0
TOTAL.	177	206

Husbands, and Wives,	33	53
Widowers, & Widows,	27	26
Single men and women	16	25
Children, ...	203	
Abortives, ...	48	
TOTAL.....	327	104

Increased in Marriages,.... 64
Decreased in Burials,...... 28
Increased in Christenings,.. 92

AGES DIED AT.

Ages Died at.	Males.	Fem's.	Ages.	Males.	Fem's.	Ages.	Males.	Fem's.
Under three Months..	24	20	Four to five	4	5	Forty to 50	15	17
Three to six	10	3	Five to ten.	14	9	Fifty to 60	8	9
Six months to 1 year..	14	18	Ten to 15..	3	10	Sixty to 70	15	16
One year to two	12	16	15 to 20...	7	8	70 to 80...	10	12
Two to three.. :	11	13	20 to 30...	6	20	80 to 90...	8	8
Three to four........	7	10	Thirty to 40	7	9	90 to 100..	2	3

TOTAL...... 177 206

Parker, Printer, Market-place.

Bill of mortality for Blackburn, 1810

same area and noted that 'one of them loses several patients every year of the puerperal fever and the other never so much as meets with disorder'.[8] The newly born infants themselves were at risk as a result of the fever. Others became blind as a consequence of neglect to wipe away the purulent discharge at birth.

For many ailments families drew on their knowledge of simple remedies. Even for town dwellers the country was close at hand, and many retained, as did the villagers, traditional knowledge of hedge and field plants. Indeed, the area had a reputation for its self-taught naturalists. Medical botany, as a doctor in one of the Pennine areas wrote, was 'the study of every rustic'. He had often seen in the cottages collections of more than thirty specimens of 'medical virtues' known to the owners which were distilled for tinctures, infusions and fomentations. He regretted that, so far as doctors were concerned, the native herbs had been largely superseded by expensive foreign drugs.[9]

With their rural background there were many ordinary folk, like Mrs Gaskell's Alice Wilson in *Mary Barton*, who were called upon for their skills.[10] Plants picked on Sundays were stored for later use against all manner of illnesses. Many of the home brews were 'loosening' medicines, as were the customary mixtures of brimstone with milk or treacle; there were other remedies: posset drinks for colds, saffron for measles, as well as plasters for many kinds of inflammation and injury.

In the towns operatives could select from an array of medicines bought from quack vendors. It was not only the artisan and labourer who were gullible. Well-to-do folk sought quick remedy from the more expensive patented compounds advertised by booksellers and apothecaries. There were various powders, pills, lozenges, nuts, syrups, tinctures, ointments and plasters, all of them said to relieve a multiplicity of complaints, including those of infancy and childhood. Sometimes more exotic drugs were purchased—gambage, calomel and scammony—which in overdose could prove fatal.[11]

Humbler householders were not tempted to such excesses, but perhaps there was little to choose between the credulity of the peasant weaver and that of the urban operative. As to how effective some of the simpler cures were, perhaps George Eliot had the answer: '. . . how can anybody know? . . . *with* a blessing . . . I've seen a mustard plaister work when there was no more smell nor strength in the mustard than so much flour. And reason good—for the mustard had lain in paper nobody knows how long—so I'll leave you to guess.'[12]

The Manchester doctors on the Board of Health had complained of the unwholesome conditions of factory children, of the prevailing dirt in their homes and hence in themselves and their clothing. Ferriar had castigated the womenfolk for their neglect of family welfare and preference for factory employment. Certainly the difficulties of washing and drying clothes must have daunted all but the most conscientious and strong-minded. In the smaller communities, however, many households, despite the shortage of water and high price of soap,[13] made great efforts. Morale was higher in the more stable settlements or amid the kinship networks of the towns where there was incentive to keep up with spring whitewashing and regular cleaning. Thus Saturday nights were customarily spent in sweeping, scrubbing and sanding floors.[14] Though homes in the industrial villages might be crowded with large families—and there were grim tales of incest and inbreeding[15]—children had the benefit of fresh air and healthier basic foods.

Everywhere the distinction was between the respectable poor and the rest. The former made great efforts to keep clean and sometimes, particularly in the villages, even to maintain the traditions of the past and provide for their children simple teaching in the rudiments.[16] The latter included newcomers to the urban areas, some of whom—among them Irish settlers—were unable to rise above poverty and filth. Their offspring suffered particularly and swelled the death rate in the towns.

It was the respectable poor who sent their children to Sunday schools, which spread rapidly from the last decades of the eighteenth century. Though primarily moral and religious in purpose, their objectives were also secular. They were necessary, according to the Bishop of Chester, whose diocese covered the manufacturing districts of Lancashire and Cheshire, to keep working children from the temptation 'to be idle, mischievous and vitious' on the Sabbath.[17] His view was evidently shared by some industrialists, including Horrocks of Preston, who for many years paid an employee to clear the streets on a Sunday and check that children attended Sunday school.[18]

Already by 1801 Manchester was holding Whit week processions of

Sunday school scholars and individual institutions were reckoning their members, who included young people and adults, by thousands.[19] Among the largest and the most famous of the early Sunday schools was that in Stockport. Rebuilt in 1805, it offered entrance to 'Any children who labour for their living in the week-day, are seven years old or upwards, and not afflicted with any contagious disease'. In the turbulent year of Peterloo instructors urged restraint on older scholars and discharged offenders. Members were to 'labour to get their own living and to do their duty in that state of life which it shall please God to call them'.[20]

Growing prosperity in the years after 1819 enabled factory folk to provide their children with Sunday footwear and clothing, boots instead of clogs, and for girls hats rather than shawls.[21] Poorer children, offspring of domestic workers, were rarely so fortunate. One recalled that his only cap was home-made from the ends of warp thread. His first shoes were so precious that he took them to bed lest they should be stolen overnight.[22] Sunday school was a spur to special effort in washing and hair-combing on the one day of the week. The memorable Sunday school treats, when spiced cake and ale were provided, served to reinforce child loyalties.[23]

In the course of time it was Nonconformist Sunday schools, particularly those associated with Methodism that were to have the greatest appeal. Wesley's own teaching had encompassed physical as well as spiritual health, and his book *Primitive Physic* had gone to twenty-nine editions by 1820. The tradition of folk herbalism which he upheld was to remain a firm feature of Nonconformity.[24] Even more important was the life style he promoted; avoidance of excess, temperance, cleanliness, fresh air and exercise. Sunday schools were the means by which generations of children were to be instructed, disciplined and also trained in standards of cleanliness. It was the view of a later medical officer, himself a product of a Methodist Sunday school, that such institutions had sustained family life, both in a practical and moral sense, and enabled people to withstand the worst effects of industrial conditions.[25]

Sunday school scholars were vast in number compared with those of the early day elementary schools, which were similarly associated with the Churches but which catered largely for the offspring of superior artisans or for very young children. They too insisted on

decent appearance. In the words of the committee of the Preston
National School in 1815, 'Let your children be clean washed and
combed—remembering that a dirty child is a disgrace to its Parents,
and that where there is a want of cleanliness in a home there will
seldom be found much regard to *morality* and *religion*.' Children with
infectious complaints were to be removed and, if their parents were
poor, were to receive free treatment.[26]

According to the principle of self-help Sunday schools afforded
assistance through their sick and burial societies. Friendly societies
had long been a feature in established trades. By the early nineteenth
century child workers as in Preston and Bolton were among the
members of local organisations.[27] Exceptionally, paternalistic
employers like Greg organised a factory sick club for which he
deducted a farthing from each shilling of wages.[28]

Mainly, however, children who sought protection joined local
Sunday school societies. The famous Bennett Street Sunday School in
Manchester had a Sick and Funeral Society from 1812.[29] Weekly
subscriptions were a farthing to qualify for the funeral allowance and
a halfpenny or a penny for sick benefit. Members, of course, had to be
regular attenders, and entry to the sick club by the young worker was
dependent on a certificate vouching for the applicant's good health
and sound constitution. From the surviving records of Bennett Street
and the neighbouring school in German Street, membership of the
funeral societies started at the age of four. Of the 335 death benefits
paid out by the former over the period 1812–42, a quarter were for
children between five and ten.

Few records of early Sunday school sick pay are available. From
Bolton it was reported in the '30s that child factory workers were less
of a burden on societies' funds than other working children.[30]
Surviving records from Manchester societies indicate that only a small
proportion of members were scholars in Class I, i.e. below teen-age.
Those claiming sick benefit were visited twice weekly by class
collectors and monthly by room collectors. Typically, cases of child
birth were excluded.

V PHILANTHROPIC ENDEAVOUR

In most families when a doctor was called it was usually as a last resort and often when it was too late. By contrast, some pauper children, inmates of the larger workhouses, and those whose families were on relief received medical attention. Samuel Bamford, whose father became master of the Manchester workhouse, described in his autobiography the care of the paupers during a severe outbreak of smallpox. Following an attack of fever, he was himself treated by the house apothecary, who gave him syrup of blackthorn, 'a nauseous and sickly drug'.[1]

Poverty was the most frequent cause of sickness and, as always, it was (in the words of a commentator of 1801) 'the modest, the bashful and really indigent' who struggled to avoid the ignominy of seeking relief.[2] He accused the Manchester overseers of pitiless treatment of cases of pregnancy. One unmarried young woman suspected of being in such condition was put 'in a conspicuous part of the room, amongst more than three hundred of the poor, four to a dish of water porridge and buttermilk . . .'.[3] Of another such woman it was reported that she gave birth on the bare flags of the lobby. She was then placed in bed alongside fever cases.[4]

Apparently the Manchester workhouse children were fed on a monotonous diet of oatmeal. As to their general condition, the boys were almost destroyed by bugs and lice in their cockloft dormitory. The girls, meanwhile, were so short of clothing that they were left almost naked when it was washed; indeed, it was claimed that the single pair of stockings allotted to each child was *never* washed but worn continuously until it was fit only for a workhouse mop head![5] After such a regime, apprenticeship to a weaver, shoemaker or even a chimney sweep must have seemed a welcome release.

In exceptional trades, where apprenticeships were much sought after by parents, master craftsmen could lay down their own conditions, which included medical care. For example, Peter Stubs, file maker of Warrington in the early nineteenth century, required in the terms of indentures that the parents should provide in addition to board, food and clothing '. . . also Doctors, Apothecaries and Nurses in cases of sickness'.[6] In less skilled trades like textiles, where child apprentices were brought in as a form of cheap resident labour, an employer like Greg of Quarry Bank, Styal, was unusual in the attention he provided. Here each ailing child was seen by the family physician, Peter Holland, whose prescription book for the period 1804–27 survives.[7] Leeches were applied in cases of inflammation of the eyes, together with blistering. There was also the customary purgative treatment with 'white powders', rhubarb, calomel and senna. Children with fever were to be isolated, and washed morning and night in water to which vinegar had been added. For injuries there were poultices of oatmeal and buttermilk, and for swollen ankles nightly rubbing with sweet oil. To build up strength and vitality nourishing broth was recommended as well as buttermilk, apple tea, sage tea and daffodil root tea. Flannel waistcoats were to be worn by those afflicted with painful coughs. On their return to the mill apprentices were to begin with light work and beforehand were to get plenty of fresh air; even in the warmer weather there was the recommendation 'to bathe twice a week in the river'.

Few children of the industrial poor received such attention. However, from the later years of the eighteenth century charitable help was available for sickness in certain urban areas. It was part of a national philanthropic movement for the foundation of dispensaries and infirmaries, including, in populous centres, lying-in hospitals.

In Manchester the Lying-in Hospital was established in 1790, the result of a break-away movement from the Manchester Infirmary started some forty years earlier. Under its founders, known as Midwives Extraordinary, the institution trained female midwives for 'the delivery of poor women at their own habitations' within closely defined boundaries, including Angel Meadow in Manchester and Paradise Court in Salford.[8] Very soon it was delivering a thousand women a year and was able to provide accommodation for exceptional maternity cases and for young children under the age of two (later raised to six to complement the work of the Infirmary).

Every application was scrutinised to ensure that charity was restricted to 'the sober and industrious Poor'. Early rules for lying-in were amended to include only respectable women and deserted wives.[9] Subscribers were assured that their contributions 'will soothe the anguish of many a tender Husband, will alleviate the agonising pains, prevent the sickness and death of many a valuable Woman and preserve the life of many a helpless Infant'. Women who were on parish relief were excluded, as were those who kept 'houses of ill-fame'. (On a later occasion when, by oversight, an illegitimate child was delivered and died, the official record noted, '. . . such cases are frequently attended with some unfortunate occurence as they are necessarily under disagreeable mental impressions and emotions'.)[10] In addition to care and wholesome food, which in many cases replaced the customary gin and strong tea, patients were instructed in religion and morality. They were taught habits of cleanliness and trained in preparation for future confinements. On discharge they were expected to attend a monthly meeting of the Governors and return thanks.

There were smaller charities for the relief of poor married women in childbed in neighbouring towns, including Preston, Stockport, Bolton, Burnley and Bury. Under the provisions of the Burnley Ladies' Charity mothers were supplied with gruel and each loaned 'a Bag of Linen containing 32 articles for one Month'. Two yards of flannel was given on the return of the bag of linen 'clean and in good order'.[11] The Bolton Lying-in Charity, established in 1798 by 'the benevolent females of the town', was responsible by 1823 for delivering some 300 annually.[12] By this date 'Ladies of the Committee', who also subscribed to the Dispensary, were able to secure the services of the Dispensary's house apothecary for urgent cases after child birth.[13] However, by the end of the decade demands on the Lying-in Charity outstripped its resources and the doctors of the town, by mutual agreement, refused to attend any below the class of respectable shopkeeper 'without instant payment for charge of delivery'.[14] Indeed, a local jury which in March 1831 recorded a verdict of 'still born' for the infant and 'death from exhaustion through protracted labour' on the mother, expressed severe disapproval of the surgeon who had been called in.[15] Apparently he had refused to act unless he first received his fee of a guinea.

In Manchester and Salford, meantime, over 4,000 births each year, half the total of the area, were covered by the services of the Lying-in Hospital. That such a proportion of the population required the assistance of public charity to bring their offspring into the world was considered by one medical authority a deplorable 'degree of degradation and destitution'.[16] In contrast to their demand for the services of the hospital as home patients or out-patients, women were reluctant to become in-patients. By 1814 there was only a single one and for a period none at all. At child birth wives preferred the reassurance of familiar surroundings to the impersonality of an institution associated in the public mind with the fear of death.

The early hospitals had cause to be sensitive about their death rate. The Manchester Infirmary itself, founded 'for the numerous sick poor in this populous part of the Kingdom', excluded under its rules children under six, together with other categories which presented special problems or were prone to high death rates: pregnant women, 'Persons disordered in their Senses' and those suffering from infections or incurable diseases. Exceptionally, however, children were admitted in cases of 'Fractures or where cutting for Stone, or any other Operation is required'.[17] In fact the very first in-patient, admitted on 3 August 1752 was a twelve-year-old boy who had 'sordid ulcers of the leg' and who on 15 January 1753 was discharged as 'Relieved'.[18]

Despite the entrance restrictions mortality rates were high. Knowledge of bacteria or sterility lay far in the future and even the vital importance of strict cleanliness was unrecognised. Thus operations were undertaken at great risk to life, wounds became infected and skin disease, colloquially referred to as St Anthony's Fire, swept through the wards. A Chester physician, John Aikin (later to become famous as a topographer of the region), published in 1771 his

Manchester Infirmary, from a picture of 1824

Thoughts on Hospitals in which he described hospital conditions in devastating terms. He warned that the visitor who had walked through the crowded wards might well regard the institution 'as a dismal prison where the sick are shut up from the rest of mankind to perish by mutual contagion'[19] and referred to the terror 'arising among the sick from the shocking view of each other's sufferings, their agonies, raving and dying groans'.[20] By implication, amendments to the rules of the Infirmary in 1791 reveal previous shortcomings: the requirement, for example, that nurses should behave with tenderness to patients, that patients should have clean sheets when admitted and thereafter every fourteen days and that the nurses should scour their wards weekly.[21] Even so, there were references from time to time to the 'offensive air' in the hospital.

From the admission register it is possible to extract the main diseases and afflictions of children and to note those who were 'restored to their Parents' as 'Cured' or 'Relieved', those who became out-patients, those who were designated 'Incurable' and those who died. Altogether about a quarter of the early in-patients were children, and they were put into adult wards. Many who were treated for a variety of 'Distempers'—consumption, sore eyes, worms, scrofula in the form of glandular neck swellings, and rickets—were only a few years old. Others were brought in with caries (ulceration of the bone), tumours and abscesses.

None of the complaints was new. Scrofula had long been common in country districts and had been often attributed to intermarriage (in fact it was the hereditary predisposition to the disease which doctors were later to stress). Rickets, diagnosed in the twentieth century as due to vitamin deficiency, was already associated with infant malnutrition and bad living conditions and had been recognised in the pre-industrial era. But these and other conditions were aggravated by the industrial environment. Indeed, rickety children with their bent limbs were colloquially referred to as factory cripples. One of the house surgeons described affected children,[22] 'Their lower limbs seemed to be a burden to them and they had such an appearance of distortion that no hope of relief could be well entertained.' It was for such conditions, where other remedies such as calomel and blistering had been tried in vain, that cod-liver oil was prescribed to good effect. Rich in fat, the oil, obtained by a primitive process, was exceedingly distasteful, 'leaving upon the palate a flavour like that of tainted fish'. As a remedy, however, it was cheap and efficient because it contained the essential but unknown vitamin. Already by the 1780s some fifty to sixty gallons were dispensed annually to both children and adults. Percival himself used cod-liver oil for adults with severe rheumatism or enfeebled by excessive labour. He had the oil emulsified with potassium carbonate; each dose was followed by a drink of lemon juice.[23]

Except in emergencies only those of the sick poor who could produce letters of recommendation from subscribers were admitted to the hospital or treated as out-patients in the dispensary. Some thirty years after the foundation of the Infirmary a system of home visiting was introduced for patients in Manchester and Salford and was subsequently extended to assistance for 'Poor Married Women In Difficult Labour'. Out-patients were forbidden to loiter about the environs of the Infirmary or to beg anywhere in the town. They received medicines free, but were required to bring back phials or gallipots before replenishment.[24]

Over the years an increasing number of child victims of accidents were admitted. Often through mishap or carelessness children were crippled by getting entangled with factory machinery. In 1799, and again five years later, by press announcements and letters to manufacturers the Infirmary urged the necessity of guarding machinery.[25] Each year the records included lists of lacerations and fractures of children who were scavengers, piecers, doffers, and winders. There were many cases of finger ends being caught in rollers and more serious accidents caused by hair and loose clothing drawn into revolving shafts.

From 1784 the Infirmary was offering inoculation against smallpox 'for children of proper objects of charity'. By means of handbills and press notices the trustees publicised the service they provided each year from September to May. They regularly lamented that so few took advantage. By 1800, two years after the publication of Jenner's discovery, they were offering daily 'inoculation for the disease of cowpox'.[26] Within six months, they reported, 400 children had received the new form of inoculation and with such successful results that the old form of inoculation was now 'entirely superseded . . . by the introduction of that mild and safe substitute, the cowpox'. The new vaccine afforded the prospect of eradicating 'a foul, painful and dangerous disease'.[27]

Simultaneously strong pressure for vaccination was put on patients of the Lying-in Hospital. Each local midwife was instructed to give the mother a ticket to present to the hospital when she took her child for vaccination. For every dozen tickets given in the midwife received 2*s*. Even so, it was rare for more than half the infants to be vaccinated. The demand for vaccination rose only with fresh outbreaks of smallpox.

Vaccination was offered by new dispensaries in local towns either free or on payment of 1s, which was refunded after a second visit. Invariably there were complaints that parents who avoided vaccination or had some unsatisfactory form of it at local druggists were imperilling their families. All the dispensaries, like the Manchester Infirmary, were intended to serve the unpauperised industrious poor. A few, like those in Stockport and Wigan, were founded at the end of the eighteenth century, but most of them opened later: Preston in 1809, Macclesfield and Bolton in 1814, Blackburn in 1824, Chorley in 1828, Salford, Bury and Ardwick and Ancoats in 1829, Chorlton upon Medlock and Hulme in 1831 and Rochdale in 1832. Few were equipped to take in-patients until after the middle of the century but all included young children as out-patients. Indeed, the medical officer at the Preston Dispensary reported in 1816, following the typhus epidemic, that whole families were struck down and that half the patients were children; similar proportions were recorded elsewhere in the '20s and '30s.[28] Children were also included in the early home visiting which each dispensary organised within a restricted area, usually a radius of a mile from the centre of the town. It was the treatment of infants and children (as well as the aged) that accounted for the high death rates. Many were babies with convulsions, others were victims of accidents or were suffering from rickets.

Some of the dispensary doctors were outspoken about the condition of factory children. From Stockport one recorded in 1819 that, of more than 800 factory children examined by himself and a colleague, barely a quarter were healthy. All the rest were delicate or diseased; some were obviously stunted and many others were suffering from enlarged ankles and knees.[29]

Except in an emergency would-be patients had to present a subscriber's recommendation, the quest for which could cause delay and distress. In cases of infection, however, as in the cholera epidemic of the '30s, an entire family was considered as a single patient. The most common child affliction was diarrhoea, which dispensary doctors attributed to the parents themselves, their dirty, slovenly and filthy practices, the accumulation of offensive materials in the vicinity of their dwellings and their general neglect of personal cleanliness. Even within the dispensaries the atmosphere of the crowded waiting rooms was poisoned by the stench of bodies. Through the years there were to be continual exhortations to people to wash. Not until water became readily available and soap cheaper was there to be real incentive to improvement.

With the growing demand for the services of dispensaries pressing appeals were made for donations and subscriptions. Help was solicited on grounds of both Christian charity and self-interest. In the words of the report of the Bolton Dispensary in 1818, 'The mansions of the great, as well as the abodes of poverty and wretchedness, are open to "the pestilence that walketh in darkness, and the destruction that wasteth as noonday" '.[30]

There were, however, many urban districts without dispensaries. Even large towns like Oldham and its neighbour Ashton under Lyne, which together had a population of over 80,000 by 1831, had no medical charity. In cases of urgency, since the Manchester Infirmary drew on subscribers over a wide area, it might be possible to secure a recommendation for treatment. In fact, so far as in-patients were concerned, the Infirmary served the region, since local dispensaries were not equipped for surgery nor for more serious medical cases. Thus it sometimes happened that beds were largely filled with patients from a distance, including factory and colliery children, while many of the sick and injured within Manchester itself were attended as home patients.

Similarly, for special needs there were separate charities which served the region. There was the Manchester and Salford Lock and Skin Hospital, whose treatment for venereal disease included women and children. There was also the Manchester Institution for curing Diseases of the Eye, whose first report in 1816 listed among patients ninety-eight infants with 'Purulent Discharge' and five who were born blind.[31] Among child patients there were large numbers with 'strumous inflammation' and many suffering from factory accidents, particularly 'wounds from shuttles'.

Outstanding among early dispensaries for the nature and scale of its work was the Dispensary for Children in Manchester. Opened in 1829, the institution was the first of its kind to be established in a provincial town. By its rules treatment was limited to children under twelve, with no restriction on locality of residence so long as they came with a subscriber's recommendation.[32] In fact most of the patients, both out-patients who attended at the early premises in Back King Street and home patients, the latter restricted to Manchester and Salford, were under two years old. Most were suffering from infections, particularly diarrhoea, as a result of misfeeding, from diseases of the skin, worms, scrofula and bronchitis. Here daily was to be seen evidence of early decline, of disease and disorders, trivial enough for most healthy infants but fatal to those enfeebled and devitalised.

In the early industrial period medical institutions were a powerful expression of charity and compassion, commended to subscribers on the grounds that they offered a 'natural security against imposture'.[33] By 1831 Manchester medical charities alone were providing for some 30,000 patients a year,[34] of whom at least a third, and probably more, were cases relating to pregnancy or children. Sometimes children were brought in for treatment from the neighbourhood or even from a distance. In local towns dispensaries were providing for increasing numbers, though overall their services were limited. However, for the majority of children outside the main centres, and for a good many within them, families in time of sickness relied on their own knowledge of folk 'simples', on the advice of a neighbour or on the offering of one of the innumerable quacks.

TWO

THE FACTORY AGE
1833–70

I CHILDREN AND INDUSTRY

With the growth of the factory system power-looms displaced hand workers. Mill towns expanded rapidly. It was said of Ashton under Lyne by the mid-century that nine-tenths of the town owed its existence to the power-loom.[1] Older settlements were transformed almost overnight at a time when, as in Stockport, a huge factory from its foundation ten feet below the bed of the river to a height of six storeys could be erected in eight weeks.[2] In the valleys, former villages and towns became 'new territories, conglomerates in "the debris" which the vast whirlpool of human affairs has deposited . . . in one of its eddies'.[3]

Despite fluctuations of trade many towns, such as Blackburn, Wigan and Rochdale, were recording population increases of 100 per cent between 1840 and 1870. During a similar period smaller boom towns like Accrington were doubling their population every ten years. Always there were families on the move. As well as those coming into the urban areas for the first time, there were operatives seeking better prospects in what they called 'a good shop'. Since they had no tools to impede them, they moved freely and sent for their families afterwards.

Many of the new aggregations were overgrown villages, remote parts of ecclesiastical parishes which, though they might have Nonconformist chapels, had neither churches nor schools.[4] In the vast parishes the custom was of mass christenings, mass confirmations and mass weddings. While the established Church remained content with such wholesale ministrations, it was little wonder that it lost ground. Old allegiances gave way before the challenge of the new Dissent, or were forgotten amid growing secularism. In the mid-'30s investigators in Dukinfield, Stalybridge and Ashton under Lyne found that only a third of all householders had Anglican affiliations and that another third were unconnected with any sect.[5] Older towns changed character as well-to-do families moved out to the periphery and were replaced by in-migrants. Hence literacy, judged by the modest standards of marriage registers of parish churches, declined dramatically.[6]

In the larger centres the poor were virtually isolated. Here, where houses were being demolished to make room for railways, offices, mills and business houses, populations became even more compressed until the amount of space per person was said to be less than that allowed to a criminal.[7] However, people continued to crowd in; by 1861 there were, for example, almost 120 to the acre in the Manchester township and 140 in Hulme. Elsewhere, too, there was the common practice of 'huddling', of sharing accommodation with lodgers. Even in industrial villages large families shared their homes so that in two-bedroom houses there were as many as ten occupants.[8]

As the largest town of the area Manchester illustrated most strikingly the growing gulf between rich and poor. Increasingly the latter were isolated in back streets, behind the public buildings and out of sight of the well-to-do shoppers and businessmen who travelled in from the suburbs and beyond. The same process was at work in other urban centres. In Salford the prosperous families were to be found in Broughton, well segregated from the densely packed areas of Greengate and Regent Road. In Preston and other towns, similarly, there was a distinction between the better parts with wide streets and the 'inferior districts' where they were down to a few yards.

In the factories work speeded up with the introduction of more efficient machinery. Mills became larger; in the early 1830s Manchester had spinning mills employing more than 1,000. As the new self-acting mules required fewer adults relative to the number of child piecers, family links were severed. By 1840 an average of four piecers were employed to every spinner in Manchester, with only 15 per cent of the children related to the adult workers.[9] Elsewhere the combination of spinning and weaving to form larger factories had the same effect. It was true that in many smaller communities, where a single factory absorbed all working members, children were identified with their families. Even so, it was more often than not a question of indirect responsibility rather than direct supervision. In the valleys there were, even at the mid-century, numerous families where the fathers worked as hand-loom weavers or on smallholdings while children went to the mills or printworks. Well before the 5 a.m. morning start they set out, the older ones carrying the five- or six-year-olds on their backs.[10]

There was conflicting evidence on the condition of factory children. Much depended on the location of the factory as well as the character of individual employers and the extent to which they exercised control of the overseers who were directly in charge of the children. Few were as concerned for the welfare of their employees as the Ashworths of Bolton, who, from the '30s, required the overseers to check that all children washed themselves thoroughly after breakfast and who had the passages between the machinery washed and 'stoned' so that they would not slip.[11]

Contemporary witnesses were often conscious of appalling conditions outside the factories. There was plenty of evidence that there were other working children worse off—sedentary ones like the little milliners' girls who were at the mercy of individual employers and the pin-headers, like those in Warrington '. . . unhappy children . . . who are of far tenderer age than any in factories and have to sit twelve hours daily at a table with their bodies continuously bent in the form of a little c, their eyes fixed upon pin heads and both hands and feet in perpetual motion'.[12] There were also, as in Rochdale, card setters, cramped in crowded workshops, and elsewhere paper makers engaged in sorting rags in an atmosphere of dirt and dust.[13] Heaviest and most dismal of all was the work of colliery children, the drawers who dragged tubs of coal from the coal face to the pit eye and the trappers who were perpetually in the darkness and the damp.

Indeed, it was suggested that where there was a choice of employment between the mines and the mills it was the stronger children who were sent to the mines and the weaker to what was considered light work in the mills.[14] One visitor, taken to selected cotton factories, was of the opinion that children's work amounted to 'mere confinement, attention and attendance'.[15] According to certain doctors, conditions were particularly favourable in silk mills, where work was light and, compared with the dust of the cotton factories, clean. 'If a poor man's child must work, it is impossible there can be employment less objectionable.'[16] There were also fewer accidents among child silk workers than in the cotton industry, since the machinery was lighter and easier to fence off. As for the deformities of factory children, they were said to be general and a result rather of the practice of tight swaddling and bandaging in infancy than of later work.[17]

However, even allowing for exaggeration, there was much cause for concern. Though in the spinning process machinery had been improved, there were particular deformities associated with throstles. The introduction of the self-acting mule required piecers to walk long distances. Fielden's calculation of twenty miles a day was probably excessive, but even Greg's more modest estimate of eight miles for children who were never off their feet throughout the hours of work represented an immense strain.[18] Premature employment, at a time when bones were imperfectly developed, as well as the conditions and long hours, accounted for twisted limbs and curved spines.

The dust and fluff of the spinning processes, including the preliminary scutching and carding, which gave rise to the term 'spinners' phthisis', affected the child workers. One of the most poignant accounts was that of a thirteen-year-old girl who in 1833 had been a power-loom weaver for two to three years but was formerly in the carding room.

This was the hardest. Then she was stuffed up in her breath, had to fight for her breath every night when she came home. A year ago her mother, thinking weaving did her harm standing on the damp flags, put her back to the card room, but it stuffed her breath again and she had jaundice, and after two or three months her mother put her back to weaving again.[19]

While thread had to be spun at high temperatures, weaving required humid conditions. With the introduction of power-looms children were employed as tenters. By the age of twelve or so they ran their own looms and were said to weave as well as men of thirty or forty.[20] They were paid at piece rates; the harder they worked the more they got. Some of the factory accidents were of child weavers who had been hit in the eye by shuttles when the yarn had broken.

Visitors were struck by the great noise of machinery as in Dickens's description of 'Coketown' (Preston), 'a rattling and a trembling all day long'. Indeed, it was the noise which the children themselves at first found terrifying, as Adam Rushton noted in his recollections of

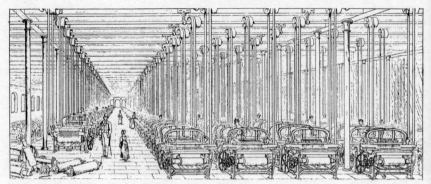

Power-loom factory in Stockport in the 1830s. From Andrew Ure, *The Philosophy of Manufactures*, 1835

starting work in a silk factory in Macclesfield at the age of eight. At first he was deafened and his fingers trembled so much that he could not fasten the silk ends together. When he had become accustomed to the delicate thread he learned to wind in swifts (reels). 'Shortly I had six of these swifts to keep going by myself. Then twelve and then twenty and more . . .' His factory day was 6 a.m. to 8 p.m., in his own words 'a murderous length of time for children to work'.[21]

Often children's injuries were attributed to carelessness when fatigue and exhaustion were the root causes. Wakened usually at 5 a.m. by the 'knocker-up', or as in Ashton under Lyne at one period by the ringing of the parish church bell,[22] they toiled through the long watches. Little wonder that they had to be driven on by the shame of wearing a badge of idleness, as in one Macclesfield silk factory, or by the rod and lash.[23]

However, physical violence was usually the reaction of the small-scale manufacturer or of the workman who hired his own labour himself. Cotton spinners were later reported to prefer children who had attended infant school because they were already disciplined and needed less beating.[24] Various ploys were used to keep children awake. One child's recollection was of the terror generated when 'a ghost-like effigy the full size of a man made of cotton was carried round the mill'.[25] In calico printworks where children, as 'teerers', sometimes worked through the night, the printers made them run around or wash their faces. However, 'teerers' on night work were known to break down, run away or go to sleep under the table.[26]

Indeed, the longest hours of factory labour were endured by such workers, girls and boys of five and upwards, according to the 1841 census, who were employed in the numerous printworks, particularly in the Burnley and Accrington region. Through the 'pushes' they were required night and day. Like automatons they stood in one position in an atmosphere of humidity and heat and sickened by the smell. Such food as they had, usually bread and treacle, was eaten on the job and handled with chemical-stained fingers.

Accidents were often due to unguarded movements in the slippery aisles between machines. They were also the result of children being set to clean machinery while it was still in motion. The loss of two or three fingers was not exceptional. There were more serious accidents, particularly to girls whose hair or flowing garments were caught in machinery. There were many examples, such as that reported by a Stockport doctor in 1840 of a girl caught by the hair and scalped from the nose to the back of the head. The manufacturer gave her five shillings. She died in the workhouse. Another Stockport girl was carried by her clothing round an upright shaft. Her thighs were broken, her ankle dislocated and she became a cripple for life.[27] There were children who fell through trap-doors, others even who were killed by blows from overseers.

Accidents confirmed the worst fears of fathers, hand-loom weavers, who had felt compelled to send their children to the mill. One such parent, whose child had been crushed to death, said he had seven sons, but if he had seventy-seven he would never send another to a cotton factory. He added bitterly, 'if they will invent machines to supersede manual labour, they must find iron boys to mind them'.[28]

However, at a time when children under the age of ten formed a quarter of the population in many urban areas there was no shortage of juvenile labour. By 1833 children under fourteen formed a fifth or a sixth of the total work force in the textile towns. There were, for example, 4,000 children in the mills in Manchester, 1,600 in Stockport, 1,500 in Bolton and 1,300 in Hyde.[29] In general, factory employment brought consistency of earnings rarely known to the domestic worker, and, with large families, children's wages helped to provide households with a better diet than would otherwise have been possible. Already by the '30s child hand-loom weavers were said to be a greater burden on sick societies than factory children.[30]

There were clearly contrasts from area to area and from family to family. There was, for example, a great difference between the condition of child piecers, members of the prosperous families of the Hyde spinners described by Edward Baines, and that of the average factory child, offspring of a labourer, in a large impersonal community. A contemporary, quoted by Baines, described the Manchester factory children as 'almost universally ill-looking, small, sickly, barefoot and ill-clad. Many *appeared* to be no older than seven.'[31]

Much depended on the factory master. At one extreme there were employers who took an active interest in children's welfare and ensured that they were regularly washed. At the other were those who pitilessly depressed living standards by the truck system under which earnings had to be taken in food, charged often at unfair rates. Thus, as Moses Heap of Rossendale remembered, wages were always bespoken and families also put to great hardship. He, along with his mother and many others, had to wait till midnight for the carrier to arrive from Burnley with provisions.[32]

The smaller manufacturers could be the most heartless. One Stockport parent explained in 1843 how two child silk workers had died. 'They were—lost as we think, by cold caught in the cockloft, an upper room where they were reeling through the windows being blown out; the draught came to their heads and it turned to consumption.'[33] The cotton mills were larger and subject to inspection. A German physician who visited Birley's manufactory in Manchester in 1844 was astonished by the scale of the weaving premises. He commented, 'The children whom we saw here, almost all girls, looked pale but in other respects not unhealthy, or neglected; some were even pretty.'[34] From the mid-century weaving sheds were loftier; even so, there was heavy dust from certain qualities of yarn which affected the lungs. Meanwhile in carding rooms consumption and pneumonia were common among 'hands' and affected particularly 'lads who had recently come from the pure country air'.[35]

Parents themselves often resisted proposals to curtail their children's hours of labour. For them, as John Doherty, editor of the *Poor Man's Advocate*, wrote in 1832, 'even the feelings of nature are destroyed or perverted, and every trace of parental affection obliterated'.[36] In society generally it was accepted as an act of God that there were children who were born weakly and would die early.

In Baines's words, 'Such children would sink under factory labour, as they would under any other kind of labour or even without labour . . . If we would abandon every occupation which may accelerate the natural tendency to disease or decay the most indispensible occupations of civilised man must be given up.'[37]

It was the unique concentration of children in textile centres and the dramatic impact made by the revelation of their conditions that brought the extension of previous regulations and the first effective legislation for the protection of child workers in 1833. Eleven years later under the half-time system two children in rota were to cover the adult working day.[38]

II CHILDREN AND THE ENVIRONMENT

One justification for child labour, expressed often with powerful conviction, was that the factory was healthier than the home, that the child was therefore better off working than at home or wandering in the streets. In contrast to the public and domestic squalor the factory was clean, dry and spacious, and afforded 'a moderate degree of healthy exercise'.[1]

On physical conditions in the main towns there is abundant evidence from the surveys of experts in the '40s. However, such towns were not the entire area; conditions in the growing villages and in urban settlements fringing the countryside were altogether healthier. Moreover the effects of social disruption were less severe in areas where traditions of community life survived.

Despite its mills the air in High Crompton, near Oldham was, according to Samuel Bamford in 1841, 'as untainted as the wind', and the homes, 'two up and two down' were spotlessly kept.[2] Among the model settlements, Ashton's at Hyde was much publicised by visitors who noted the 'ruddy countenances' of the factory folk and compared them with the 'sickly, pallid' faces of the Manchester operatives.[3] There were similar settlements elsewhere, organised according to a 'village mill paternalism'. Thus in the industrial 'colony' of Samuel Greg (junior) at Bollington, significantly named Goldenthal, workers' homes were well-lighted and provided with gardens and sanitation, and there were also a school, playing fields and other amenities.

Such arrangements were exceptional. Often homes in outlying areas were as cramped and congested as those in the towns. Nevertheless children had not only fresh air but also a wholesome diet which included milk and oatmeal porridge, cheese and meat. In contrast the food in the larger centres in the 1830s was usually bread, potatoes, strong tea and bacon quickly cooked. The fare which Adam Rushton described—for Sunday dinner at his Hurdsfield home near Macclesfield, 'a cut of beef and potatoes' followed by apple or gooseberry dumpling—was filling and nutritious.[4] Even the home-baked fruit dough cakes which he took to work, though barely satisfying, were more nourishing than the bread and treacle carried by most urban children.

It was the rapid expansion of towns, their ever-increasing density and squalor and the disease associated with them that called forth a full-scale investigation. They were situated often in narrow valleys, overhung with smoke. Growth was unplanned so that the main thoroughfares became more and more congested. For 'hands', who needed to live within walking distance of their work, streets of back-to-back houses were hastily built. In older areas there were houses which could be converted into 'back-to-backs' and so halved in size. 'What a family had saved in rent they had lost in health.'[5] There were even, as in Preston, 'double houses', that is, 'back-to-backs' which also included cellar dwellings. Preston was one of the older centres which became ever more compact as more and more streets were built with narrow alleyways and courts.[6]

Sometimes the new back-to-backs were in double rows with a pump at one end and a privy at the other. In the less fortunate areas people had no water at hand and no sanitation. An official described in the mid-'40s conditions in three streets in Colne housing 500 families of factory workers. 'There is not one privy belonging to all their dwellings! ... I know of nothing greater than the filthiness and indecency of Colne.'[7]

In evidence of physicians on sanitary conditions in the towns in 1842 there were many descriptions of unpaved streets afloat with refuse and of rivers which, polluted by sewage, wound their way sluggishly through built-up areas. Sometimes water had to be fetched from a distant pump, or bought from water-carriers at three gallons a penny.[8] For washing and scouring, buckets of water were brought from the rivers and canals and often kept for long periods until they stank. Since carrying the water, usually the job of children, was arduous and time-consuming, the temptation was to cut down on its consumption. For bathing, again there were the canals. Preston alone had a park.[9]

Though outnumbered by back-to-back houses, there remained in the older centres many cellar dwellings, three, four, even up to nine feet below ground level and let cheaply. Manchester had over 4,000 of them, Bolton 1,200, Stockport 1,000, while neighbouring towns each had several hundred.[10] In Manchester alone there were 18,000 people living in cellars, 12 per cent of the working population. In *Mary Barton* Elizabeth Gaskell described the children of a cellar family rolling on the wet brick floor.[11] It was in such conditions that bricks had to be placed under the beds in cellars to keep them dry.

Wherever the Irish settled they continued the peasant custom of keeping pigs, even in living quarters. With the quickening rate of influx distinct areas of towns became Irish ghettos. Such, for example, was Scholes in Wigan, where according to sample surveys in 1851 seven-eighths of the inhabitants of certain streets were Irish, living ten to a house. Overall the average age of death in Scholes was eighteen.[12] As hand-loom weavers, labourers, hawkers, street traders and the like, Irish families were generally poverty-stricken and depressed. Even in the '30s 'Irish fever', a form of typhus, was endemic in their districts. Always there were Irish among the numerous vagrants, adults and children who sought refuge in the workhouses or who 'in promiscuous herds' bedded down in the straw and shavings of lodging houses. Such habitations were a continual source of infection and their lodgers were condemned as social pests, responsible for outbreaks of smallpox, fever and measles.

While poisonous stenches were diluted by fresh air in the country, in the towns the odour of the privy middens, sewers and slaughterhouses pervaded the stagnant atmosphere until washed away by the rain. As John Leigh, surgeon and Registrar in the Deansgate area later observed of Manchester, 'Nothing but the constant rain makes a residence within its bounds tolerable.'[13] Violent thunderstorms were particularly welcome as the only means of cleansing the filth and decomposing matter from public thoroughfares and courts. In the smaller industrial communities, without drainage and dependent for water on springs or wells, which ran out in the dry summers, fevers were constant. Throughout the area meteorology was all-important and years of low rainfall had a devastating effect on life. As one physician wrote sadly of the overgrown village of Bacup 'People strive against filth and the filth swiftly overwhelms them.'[14]

Expectation of life was directly related to locality. In the general area, Bolton with its wider streets and supply of good water was less unhealthy than most towns. In Ashton under Lyne a clear distinction was noted between mortality rates of workers in sewered and unsewered streets. Of child factory workers in Manchester the record of ill-health and death was worst among those who lived in Ancoats and St George's.[15]

Investigation of Sunday schools, where children spent many hours on the Sabbath, revealed conditions of overcrowding. One report described 340 children in a single room so small that they were scarcely able to move.[16] While some schools were as large and lofty as factories, other were held in dingy subterranean rooms. The famous Lower Mosley Street School in Manchester for many years occupied a cellar, a former cotton warehouse. Among the scholars, some who came from a distance brought their dinner and spent the whole day there.[17] Sunday schools were often kept at the same temperature as the mills for the sake of the factory children and seemed suffocatingly hot to visitors. In one case 'all the glass windows were covered with condensed vapour'.[18]

Even more unsavoury were the so-called dame schools, much patronised as child-minding establishments. Some were in cellars, others were over stables or looked out on to open cess pools. Among the elementary schools there were descriptions of children being carried out in a faint, occurences at which, as was reported from Preston, 'the visitor who feels the contaminated stale air on entering . . . from the pure atmosphere, cannot be astonished'.[19] As for the factory children, for whom lessons were compulsory, they were often to be found in coal-holes or some dirty corner where they were 'thick as they could stand'.[20]

Of evidence on the people themselves and their home life there is little 'from below'. Often those who wrote in retrospect had moved away and may not have been typical. There are glimpses in dialect sketches and, from stories handed down, much is embedded in folk memory of the experiences of ordinary individuals. Overwhelmingly descriptions are 'from above', from assiduous surveys of the Manchester Statistical Society, from local doctors and clergymen as well as outside observers.

James Kay, medical officer at the Ardwick and Ancoats Dispensary and himself reared in the area, wrote in 1832 of

> the original, quaint, honest, and enduring population of the Lancashire homesteads and hand-looms,—a race full of rare qualities,—hardy, broken to toil, full of loyalty to the traditions of family and place,—genial, humorous, but coarse,—easily tempted by drink to hurtful excesses, and in periods of prolonged and pinching want apt to be goaded to tumult . . .[21]

Mingled with the native elements were in-migrants from near and far. Kay's fiercest denunciations were of the ignorance, recklessness and immorality of the 'mixed' population of the central township of Manchester. Others expressed horror at what they regarded as the barbarism of people in neighbouring towns. Many clergy, appointed to the new churches in the '40s, felt they were in hostile territory. They spoke of their charges as 'wretched', 'profligate', 'rude' and 'uncultivated' and saw themselves as missionaries who needed to tame and civilise before they could conquer spiritual apathy and desolation.[22] By contrast, Elizabeth Gaskell, the Manchester novelist, minister's wife and herself a mother, wrote of the struggles of factory folk, of the loyalty and affection within families and the warmth of relationships between neighbours.

Poor though most people were, their poverty was relative. Incomers had been attracted by the prospects of a livelihood, and most commentators had more to say about popular extravagance and waste than poverty. In standards of living the comparison was between, at the one extreme, the families of skilled workmen, the mechanic, overlooker or fine cotton spinner and, at the other, those of casual labourers or widows. The former might expect to own their own houses and equip them with mahogany rather than deal furniture; indeed, in good times ordinary cottages were 'crammed with furniture'. They were very likely members of provident societies and had money in savings banks. The latter had a hand-to-mouth existence and were the first to suffer in periods of depression.

Even the steady labourer 'of sober and industrious habits' with a family to keep could barely manage, and in times of rising prices was said to be 'going back in the world' (in debt) each week. In a series of case studies of workers' households in Manchester and Dukinfield in 1836 and 1841, Edward Neild, Mayor of Manchester, found that income per head varied between 9s 8d and 2s 6½d a week. The best-off, a machine printer's family, was able to spend 10-15 per cent of income on meat and substantial amounts on butter and coffee. At the other end of the scale a labourer's family lived mainly on bread, on which almost 40 per cent of earnings were spent.[23]

In general it was widows' families who were worst off. One charitable organisation in Manchester found that widows numbered up to 15 per cent of heads of families on its lists.[24] With no reserves it was particularly widows with their children who in bad times crowded into the workhouses. Of the many children who were orphaned or abandoned some were taken in by kin, others became the flotsam of the streets or the inmates of workhouses or industrial schools.

Whatever the cause of family disruption or misfortune, children were prime sufferers. Some perished at the time of migration, others were victims of parental drunkenness or disease. There were babies suffocated by drunken parents—there was always a noticeable increase in the incidence of overlaying at weekends—as well as infants and children who died of neglect or congenital weaknesses. Huge amounts of money were spent on drink in beer-houses and taverns, which, according to calculations in 1838, were in the ratio of one for each 100 to 250 of population in Bury, Ashton, Stalybridge and Dukinfield.[25] There was also home-brewed beer, drunk by both sexes. One report was of Dukinfield women who indulged in 'butty brees', Saturday-night drinking of the strong home brew, after which they were to be seen at seven o'clock on Sunday mornings staggering home.[26]

The female population of the factory districts came in for the fiercest and most persistent criticism. They were accused of fecklessness, of incapacity as home-makers and of neglect of children in preference to wage-earning. They were said to be thriftless and untidy, incapable of cooking, patching or mending. In the words of a Manchester physician, '. . . they make wretched wives'.[27]

In contrast to the denunciations of working wives by many 'experts' who would, if they could, have banned mothers from factory work, was the view expressed later by a Rochester medical officer:

. . . in the past the woman who toiled all day and endeavoured to do her best for her home and family, has not received from man in his wisdom or selfishness the sympathetic consideration which the importance of her work and duties demanded. For after all, such women are the salt of the earth, and have played no unimportant part in the building up of the great industries of Lancashire.[28]

The fact was that within families girls were born to work; any opportunity for apprenticeship or schooling went to male offspring. Even by the modest standard of marriage signatures brides were less literate than grooms.[29] Investigators were quick to link their 'disgracefully low education' with excessive infantile mortality.[30]

However, the proportion of working wives with young children was probably smaller than might be assumed from the frequent references to them. Sample surveys have indicated that there were about 20 per cent at the mid-century in Preston and possibly smaller percentages in some of the industrial villages.[31] Stockport seems to have been exceptional, with an increasing proportion after the mid-century and even a majority recorded in samples by 1861.[32] Many working mothers had relatives living with them to look after the children; others called on those near by or on friends or neighbours. It was noted that, compared with the rest of the country, there were few elderly women dependent on the poor rates.[33] They assisted in the homes and even carried hot dinners to the mills. In more impersonal surroundings, however, working wives were compelled to leave their offspring with 'minders' and it was here that some of the worst cases of neglect occurred.

The sort of complaints levelled at working wives and mothers in the factory areas were heard elsewhere. Certainly in the 1840s working colliery wives were condemned as severely for their lack of domesticity, for their 'ill-kept homes' and 'rough and ready ways'.[34] Criticism on grounds of premature marriage is hardly borne out by statistics, which show higher proportions of under-age brides elsewhere, both on the Durham coalfield to the north and among the Staffordshire pottery and metal workers to the south.[35] Nor were illegitimacy rates significantly higher than in other industrial areas and, possibly because of the ease of concealment, were lower than in rural districts. Many of the commentaries were subjective; they stressed the bride's lack of foresight, though rarely the groom's; in the words of one observer, the girl 'marries as other people take a day's holiday. Her wedding is a pleasant little incident in her life, and the next day she goes to work as usual.'[36]

Consciously or subconsciously many middle-class observers compared factory wives with women who had been in domestic service and found them by comparison poor managers. There was awareness of the very same problem in other trades, however, as illustrated by instructions in 1840 to commissioners investigating child employment outside textiles. They were to enquire of females 'How far their employment during childhood had prevented them forming the domestic habits usually acquired by women in their station . . .'.[37] Similarly, a high infantile death rate—again associated with working mothers—was not peculiar to textile districts. It was a feature of towns like Coventry and Nottingham and of the rural eastern counties where females worked in agricultural gangs.[38]

There was some evidence to suggest that in the crowded insanitary areas of the textile districts women who stayed at home had less resistance to epidemics than wage-earners. Among adults the higher death rate of females from cholera in both 1832 and 1849 was attributed to their confinement within the household.[39] (It was noted in 1849 that young children were similarly affected and their death rate rose as a consequence of 'choleraic diarrhoea.')[40] Again it was among the overcrowded, underfed populations that the most severe effects of the cotton famine were felt. As early as 1862 typhus carried off adults over a wide area, while, in Manchester and Salford particularly, the years which followed brought a high child death rate from scarlet fever.[41]

During the same period the infant death rate fell noticeably, however. To outsiders it was a curious paradox that the former years of prosperity and abundance should have proved more deadly than a period of protracted hardship. The reduction in infant mortality was quoted as proof that maternal care outweighed the effects of poverty. The same evidence was, of course, also a vindication of the mothers in the factory districts, testimony to their resilience in adapting to hardship and most of all to their self-sacrifice so that children should be the last to suffer.[42] Crises such as the cotton famine and the earlier depression of the '40s were a great test of family feeling and evoked expressions of affection in people who were not usually demonstrative.

There was the reply of the destitute Stockport mother who refused in 1841 the only form of relief offered by the Guardians, namely that her children should go to the workhouse; '. . . you may as well take my life as my children; I would rather die than part with 'em . . .'.[43]

The general standards of care in ordinary times varied widely. On the one hand we hear of mothers who rarely changed their children's clothes so that they 'wear the same thing day after day for weeks together', on the other there were descriptions of those who in the most desperate circumstances kept their homes 'as clean as could be expected'. Certain habits came to light by chance, for example from the puzzled male reactions when the Cotton Famine Relief Committee provided nightshirts, since by custom only females wore special nightwear.[44] There were inhibitions that were well known, such as the sheer terror of fresh air which caused families to nail up windows and exclude ventilation.

During trade depressions there were heart-rending stories of destitution and suffering when people pawned almost all their possessions. One Stockport pawnbroker described in 1841 how children, 'bare-footed and bare-headed', accompanied their mothers and begged them to sell whatever they had in order to buy bread or potatoes. Another reported a father who came with his four-year-old son and sold his spectacles for twopence. Though the loss left him half-blind, he said, 'I am like to do without them. I am like to have something for belly for myself and Boy.'[45]

As each depression receded, however, trade picked up quickly and families felt the benefit. By 1851 signs of prosperity were evident from the numbers of retailers and craftsmen listed in census returns. As well as butchers, grocers, chemists and druggists, even in the smaller industrial communities there were numerous shoemakers (quite distinct from cobblers and cloggers), dressmakers, milliners and bonnet-makers. David Chadwick, in a publication of the Manchester Statistical Society, calculated that over a period of twenty years, between the '30s and the '50s, wages had advanced 10–25 per cent. Boys were now earning on average 7s and girls 5s. Prices had come down, often by as much as a fifth.[46] Not only had meal and flour become cheaper, former luxuries like tea and sugar were more plentiful. Meanwhile the abolition in 1853 of the duty on soap, the so-called 'tax on washing', made cleanliness easier.

The Clitheroe weaver John O'Neil (John Ward) noted with some satisfaction in his diary in 1859, 'We have better clothes and better things in the home.'[47] O'Neil, who lived near the countryside had a healthier diet than most town dwellers. Though meat consumption had increased, their staple food was white bread which in the refining process lost much of the iron content. Large families in Manchester bought as many as thirty 4 lb loaves weekly.[48] Here in 1857, an investigation of foods commonly consumed—coffee, flour, oatmeal and bread—revealed that a third were adulterated.[49] In fact among children rickets was attributed by one medical authority to the adulteration of bread.[50] Similarly the pale, sickly appearance of many women and 'green sickness' (chlorosis) among adolescent girls were a consequence of anaemia, ascribed to confinement and to lack of nutritive food.[51]

In all the towns there were the more desirable areas and the more notorious districts. Even in the latter, however, adjacent families were very different, the drunken and dirty alongside the clean and respectable—the latter often proud to show visitors a display of their children's Sunday school prizes.[52] Perhaps those who freely stressed the errors of the mothers' ways were less perceptive than Lord Shaftesbury, who diagnosed as 'the great want of the age . . . a new generation of fathers and mothers'.[53]

III CHILD MORTALITY AND DISEASE

However subjective the judgements on married life, there was no doubt about high marriage and fertility rates. Peter Gaskell reported the 'well-known fact . . . that a woman who is not fruitful is unfit for a wife . . .'.[1] A high birth rate was accompanied by high infantile mortality. According to Lyon Playfair's investigations in 1843 the death rate in Preston for children under five had risen from a third to a half between 1783 and 1841. Three-quarters of those who died under five were less than two years old. They were cut off before they were weaned, 'so that mothers are soon in a condition again to add to their families'. 'Excessive mortality' was a 'direct cause in the production of excessive births'.[2]

His conclusions were corroborated by evidence from Roberton on Manchester.[3] Over the Manchester township as a whole the infantile death rate was more than twice that of Dorset. For one-to-two-year-olds, an age group subject to infection, it was four times as high. Thereafter the chances of life were nearly the same. Roberton contrasted the high birth rate in Hulme, a factory area, of 1 in 29·91 with that of residential Broughton—1 in 36·48. In 1841 Hulme, together with the other factory areas of Chorlton and Ardwick, had a deathrate from measles alone of 9 per cent of total deaths. It was little wonder that there was 'wholesale migration' of middle class families out of such districts. As one medical officer later put it, 'No man who wishes to keep his children in health will, if he can help it, expose them during the hotter portion of the year to an atmosphere like that of Manchester.'[4] The well-to-do retreated from the smells and from the smoke which hung everywhere and literally blackened the bronchial glands.

Differential surroundings and standards of care were clearly reflected in child mortality rates. In Preston in 1843, 18 per cent of children under five died among the gentry and professional class, 38 per cent in the tradesman class and 55 per cent in the operative class. Average ages of death were forty-seven, thirty-two and eighteen respectively.[5] Just a few miles away agricultural labourers were as long-lived as the more prosperous tradesmen of Preston. In the adjacent county of Westmorland the population of the old-established market town of Kendal had an average expectation of life twice that of people in industrial towns to the south.[6] Investigators concluded, 'the agricultural class is more near what nature made it; the other presents us with a rapid succession of stunted and debilitated families . . .'.[7]

Wide discrepancies in mortality rates between social classes were a continuing feature. In his later official capacity as Medical Officer of Health for Manchester John Leigh was to draw the attention of the city council to glaring contrasts.[8] There were the low child death rates in the Quaker community, 'whose habits of life and customs . . . would afford to the children born amongst them the best chance of survival irrespective of climate and other uncontrollable conditions'. In Manchester over the ten-year period 1859–69 there were 132 births in Quaker families and seventeen deaths of children under the age of five, of whom just seven were infants. During the same period the general death rate for young children in the city was almost 50 per cent.

With high fertility rates there were unwanted pregnancies. Abortion was by drugs and by the use of instruments. According to Stockport evidence, it was 'sadly common particularly among unmarried women and among married women living apart from their husbands'. Infanticide by means of arsenic was known to take place on a considerable scale, with the quiet disposal of unwanted infants.[9] Since the law was vague there was reluctance to give evidence. In 1861, for example, there were 176 inquests in Manchester and the surrounding area, but even when the verdict was 'wilful murder' no action was taken.[10] Often it was impossible to trace those responsible when newly born children were abandoned to their fate. Typical entries among coroners' lists are of infants 'Found in a Petty in a Back Yard', 'Found floating in the canal', 'Found buried in a small box'.[11]

Quite apart from the disposal of unknown numbers of unwanted infants, death rates, recorded in the Registrar General's reports from 1839, were depressing. Dr Farr's commentary in 1846 quoted a report from Manchester:

How pitiful is the condition of many thousands of children born in this world! Here in the most advanced nation of Europe—in one of the largest towns of England—in the midst of a population unmatched for its energy, industry, manufacturing skill—in Manchester . . . where Percival wrote and Dalton lived—13,362 children perished in seven years over and above the mortality natural to mankind.[12]

The peak death rate was at birth or immediately after. Apart from those associated with the Manchester Lying-in Hospital or one of the small local charities, midwives were self-trained. Just how numerous still-births were was unknown, since they were interred without funeral rites. It was said of certain midwives that they enquired whether a living child was desired or not; for a still-born child the charge was higher.[13]

Medical authorities made scathing references to the 'foolish . . . prejudices' of women in employing ignorant and incompetent midwives. The latter, as Farr wrote in 1841, expressed 'peculiar views of their own which they lose no opportunity of announcing and carrying into effect with the best intentions in the world, but the worst consequences'.[14] Unskilled treatment, however, was not confined to the self-appointed midwife. In Stockport subscription to the local Board of Health entitled members to professional attendance in emergencies, but, in a case reported in 1842 of an illegitimate birth, death occurred because the surgeon merely sent his apprentice, an inexperienced lad of sixteen or seventeen.[15] He put in an appearance for only ten minutes. He did not bind up the body of the mother or bring away the whole of the placenta though he informed the women present that 'all was right'. After complaints following the death of the mother it transpired that the lad was incapable of removing the placenta, though he had attended at least a dozen cases of childbirth.

There were infants who were born with only a slight chance of survival, possibly because the mother was exhausted with repeated pregnancies. Of the mothers who attended as out-patients at the Manchester Clinical Hospital, founded at the mid-century, many had lost up to ten children. In 1857 one of the early patients who had already buried twenty infants had her twenty-first child. Not surprisingly, the infant died in an emaciated condition.[16]

There were also those born with a hereditary predisposition to disease. In Farr's words, 'from the first throb of life . . . there is besides the upward, the onward impulse, a principle which draws a certain number within the sphere of disease and mortality'.[17] Under the worst conditions infants were born with cumulative disadvantages. Altogether infants and young children were most vulnerable to disease. In the first two years of life it was boys who succumbed most easily. Of the premature births more males than females died. Farr explained in 1860, '[They] die of malformations; the evolution of the male is more elaborate and is more frequently left incomplete in the male than the female . . .'.[18] As infants boys continued to be weaker than girls and generally more susceptible to infections.

In the burial records numerous infant deaths were attributed to inflammation of the lungs or of the chest. The most commonly reported cause of fatality, however, was often the consequence of misfeeding or drugging. (There were midwives who taught mothers to brew mixtures of sleeping tea.)[19] Misfeeding was also responsible for diarrhoea which, when it reached its highest peak in the hot dry summers, was the greatest single cause of infantile death. Babies who were bottle-fed or, as happened in many instances, were offered moistened bread, so-called 'pobbies', or 'bits and sups' of whatever was going, were particularly affected. In areas fringing the country skimmed milk was bought, but in the larger towns milk, sold in shops or by hawkers, cost as much as fourpence a quart and was usually so stale and impure that it quickly went sour. Many of the digestive troubles arose from ignorance and uncleanliness. There were, for example, descriptions of feeding bottles encrusted with curdled milk.[20] Infants exposed to such conditions developed not only diarrhoea but rickets, worms, gastric fever and skin diseases.

Whether from need or threat of dismissal mothers frequently returned to work early after childbirth. Some tried to combine breast feeding with factory routine. A Manchester physician described a not uncommon pattern. The mother suckled her child before setting off for work well before 6 a.m.; possibly she returned either to her own house or to a neighbouring child-minder at midday, and again fed it at home after work. By the evening, however, the child would suck so greedily as to be sick, and when the pangs of hunger reappeared the mother was unable to satisfy them and the child screamed with colic.[21]

Often she gave up the struggle to breast-feed and tried to put her child out to a wet nurse. In Ashton under Lyne one woman related how she had herself 'nursed and suckled as many as three children at a time; that she had frequently been so exhausted by it as to be unable to walk across the room; and that the children had often been so helpless under such treatment, as to be almost unable to move their hands and feet'.[22] Usually, however, the mother left her child with an elderly relative or neighbour. As time passed infants might be left at home in the care of older sisters. In fine weather such children with their charges could be seen at any hour of the day in the streets or sitting on doorsteps where infants were exposed to draughts. On colder days they were confined indoors. In one such home in Ashton there were, according to a contemporary description,

... two or three squalid children sprawling on the flags near the fire in danger of being burnt; two or three young nurses and their friends playing at shuttlecock, and disorder everywhere. The floor covered with water, ashes and excrementitious nastiness; and in the window bottom, near to a pewter teaspoon ... a small glass phial, labelled 'Street's Infants' Quietness'.[23]

'Quietness' or 'Mother's Blessing', together with 'Godfrey's', were among the mixtures containing laudanum or opium which stilled fretful cries or screams of pain. According to the individual druggist they contained from one and a half to two ounces of pure laudanum to the quart. Perhaps initially a pennyworth of 'Godfrey's' was bought from the druggist or one of the little shops nearby. As the infant needed more and still more, a stronger sleeping-tea was made at home with aniseed, treacle, sugar and laudanum. When laudanum was too expensive there were substitutes. In Clitheroe poppy heads were used; in Rochdale, a mixture of solid opium, anise and canary seed was boiled with sugar and treacle.[24] In Chorlton one doctor computed that infants of seven and eight months were taking within twenty-four hours up to fifty drops of laudanum, the equivalent of two grains of solid opium.[25]

Everywhere the child accustomed to being drugged was instantly recognisable. It became, said a contemporary, 'so thin that you see nothing but bone. Its eyes get sunken and fixed, its nose pinched, in fact such children look exactly like old wizened men and women'. There were poignant descriptions of young children who relished the sweet flavour of the mixture so much that, when taken to the shop for their 'Godfrey's', they eagerly stretched out their hands for the bottle.[26]

Sometimes infants died suddenly of convulsions as a result of overdosing. In Ashton and Oldham within a single year between 600 and 700 deaths were attributed to convulsions.[27] More commonly death came 'slowly, painfully and insidiously', infants went into a decline and were registered as dying of atrophy or wasting disease. Some fell victim to a trivial disorder because they had no resistance. Others survived but became rickety, stunted in body and with crooked limbs and unsightly joints.

Apart from diarrhoea, of the main infections (officially termed 'zymotic' diseases from 1839) mortality from whooping cough was highest in the first year of life, from measles in the second and from scarlet fever in the third. Regarded as the natural diseases of childhood, many families felt that the sooner children had them the better. 'The poor,' wrote Elizabeth Gaskell, 'are fatalists with regard to infection; and well for them it is so, for in their crowded dwellings no invalid can be isolated.'[28]

The custom of encouraging children to kiss dead siblings, including those who had died of infection, was not confined to poorer families. It was, however, among them that little heed was taken of symptoms of diseases like 'chink-cough' where children wandered at will. Whooping-cough was often fatal, particularly to those who had rickets. (Perhaps families who called in a doctor found his remedies, usually leeching and blistering, of dubious value.)

Children with measles were similarly allowed outside and not only passed on the infection but were themselves exposed to the danger of pneumonia. Examination of registers of interment in working-class areas in the mid-'30s show that between January and March each year measles was the main cause of child deaths.[29] After the peak winter figures the mortality rate fell rapidly.

By 1840 scarlet fever, which had been relatively mild in the earlier part of the century, had become malignant and, like measles, cyclical in its onslaughts. Every two or three years when numbers of children had ceased to be immune the disease struck with full force. The death rate was high in all classes of society. (Even Dr Tait, later Archbishop of Canterbury, lost five of his seven children from scarlet fever within a month in 1856.)[30]

Infection was worst during the peeling stage when the child had apparently recovered and was moving about. The fine scaling skin showered everywhere and, apart from the immediate infection, was harboured in cracks of floors and among garments which were laid aside with a change of weather. Isolation had long been recognised as a means of arresting the fever but the facility was rare. Usually it was confined to Poor Law infirmaries, and there was little hope of persuading parents to make use of them.

Though the incidence of smallpox was diminishing there were explosive outbreaks. In the autumn of 1835, for example, 158 infants and young children who had died of it were interred in the Rusholme burial ground.[31] At the end of the '30s a national epidemic struck with particular severity the textile areas which were suffering from trade depression. Again children were the main victims and, at the height of the epidemic, deaths in the North-west were a third of the national total. Thereafter as a virulent disease it was largely superseded. Of infectious diseases Farr wrote, 'when one is rooted out, it is apt to be replaced by others, which ravage the human race whenever the conditions of healthy life are wanting. They have this property in common with weeds and other forms of life; as one species recedes, another advances.'[32]

An infection newly diagnosed was diphtheria. First listed separately from croup as a throat disease by the Registrar General in 1855, it remained something of an enigma for years. Doctors not only found it difficult to diagnose, they were also doubtful about treatment. A variety of external applications were tried, leeches, blistering and tincture of iodine, as well as medicine such as quinine, acetic acid and cod-liver oil;[33] incision by tracheotemy was sometimes performed, but was considered difficult and dangerous.

Croup itself had long been recognised as painful and serious. In some years it had caused almost as many deaths as smallpox. Associated with exposure to cold and dampness, it was particularly prevalent in the Lancashire towns. Sudden attacks, it was noted, frequently came on at the weekend following the grand scrubbing and 'tubbing' which left damp floors and walls.[34] The ringing cough and the shrill sound of breathing were unmistakable. So high were the risks that, according to calculations in Manchester and Salford in 1864, death occurred in one out of every two or three cases.[35] Just how seriously croup was regarded in middle-class households is revealed in a letter by Elizabeth Gaskell in 1838.[36] She described her alarm when her eldest child was seized with an attack. 'I heard a cough which, though I had never heard croup, I felt sure must be croup.' With prompt attention—the father went to the Infirmary for immediate assistance—her daughter pulled through but another child of their acquaintance was less fortunate.

While the death rate from infectious diseases fluctuated violently from year to year, depending on the weather and the degree of immunity, fatalities from the so-called constitutional diseases varied less. These included cases of respiratory disease, much affected by the smoke and 'the blacks', flakes of carbon which blighted even the vegetation. Young constitutions suffered also from the general dirt and lack of fresh air both inside the home and in the congested courts and alleys. Lung disease, including pneumonia, was a result of exposing infants to violent changes of temperature, particularly in the early morning when they were taken from their cots into the streets. Children under the age of five were said to be the greatest sufferers from pneumonia.[37]

It was frequently earlier weakness, including the effect of measles and whooping-cough, which left children predisposed to pulmonary tuberculosis, the cause of many deaths in later adolescence. Forms of tuberculosis were a direct consequence of infected milk, of poor environment or of conditions of work. In Macclesfield and other silk districts, for example, child piecers suffered particularly from tuberculosis as a result of constant stooping.[38] Everywhere in its incipient stages as scrofula it was visible in diseased bones and joints and enlarged glands. In its intestinal forms (tabes mesenterica) tuberculosis was a wasting disease.

Though more males than females died in infancy, from the age of two the sexes were on a more equal footing. Diphtheria was one of the few diseases to which girls were more prone. At the stage of childhood, five to ten years, the female death rate was actually higher than the male, possibly because girls, kept in the home as skivvies, had less freedom to run about or because they were thought to need less food.

There were deaths which were deliberately planned, as well as others from neglect or misadventure. The town clerk of Stockport gave evidence in the early '40s on deaths from arsenic poisoning.[39] He quoted the cases of two related families of hatters and mat makers who poisoned four female children. The male children were spared, apparently because the parents considered them more likely to be useful. Always there were deaths from accidents. Frequently children were burnt or scalded to death; sometimes they were burnt at work or even at school, where infants huddled round the open fires, but usually, as coroners' records reveal, they perished of burns or by scalding in their own home. In mortality registers there are references to a great variety of misadventures: toddlers who were 'overrun' in the streets, children killed by flagstones or falls or who died by drowning, young chimney sweeps who had suffocated in flues and, above all, factory children killed by machinery or by steam boilers exploding.[40]

IV FAMILY SELF-HELP

It was the expense of calling in a doctor that deterred many families. Some, however, were prepared to pay when trade was good. Workhouse doctors who also had their own practice noted that in bad times those who had formerly paid to consult them came instead as out-door patients of the Union.[1] With children, consultations often came too late to help. There were pathetic cases referred to the corner, such as the death in October 1853 of a four-year-old in Stockport. The parents had gone to the doctor and told him the symptoms: he had diagnosed worms of the stomach, for which he had given them two lozenges and had charged 1s 6d. The child died shortly afterwards.[2]

Evidence about the home medicaments on which many families relied for child ailments is fragmentary. An enquiry in the early 1840s of Manchester schoolchildren—a selective sample, since the poorest did not attend day school—revealed that half were treated solely by their parents, who used salts, senna, magnesia, cream of tartar, rhubarb and herbs made into tea. Some, when very ill, had received medicine from a druggist and only 10 per cent had been taken to the Infirmary.[3]

Everywhere there were numerous quacks, universally condemned as charlatans by medical men. Some travelled from town to town and advertised their special skills. There were even 'surgeons' who offered instant cures for squint and stammering.[4] A few well known local men enjoyed a high reputation. Most distinguished as healers and bone-setters were the Taylors of Whitworth, originally farriers, who over several generations were widely consulted. Children who had found no relief for their deformities from surgeons were frequently taken to them from a distance. Under the 'Whitworth system' club-footed children were put in boots with iron soles and iron supports, the combined work of the village shoemaker and blacksmith. These they wore night and day during a period of residence in the village. Children with spinal deformities wore special whalebone stays.[5] The Taylor family business included a branch at Oldfield Lane, Salford. Here, as in Whitworth, there were regular surgeries. One observer recalled the scene in the 1830s. There were skins of leather hanging up, spread with 'a brown kind of plaister' from which strips were cut to bind up a broken limb or dislocated shoulder; there were also stone medicine bottles, filled with liniment known as 'Whitworth Red Bottle' and apparently for universal application.[6]

Many families collected and brewed their own herbs, which were taken to cure fevers or as tonics, or for 'loosening' purposes. Others, still close enough to their rural past to hanker for natural remedies, patronised herb dealers. During the middle years of the century there was even a flourishing and well organised herbal society, associated with the American botanist, A. I. Coffin. From its headquarters in Manchester stocks were distributed to local branches linked with Methodist chapels, and individuals were designated to advise and prescribe the various roots and herbs.[7] Clearly Coffinism as a 'scientific' form of herbalism made a powerful appeal, particularly to sober, respectable families. Even in the later years of the century, long after the society itself had disappeared, there were references to individuals from former strongholds like Oldham administering drugs 'associated with Coffinism'.[8]

From the discrimination with which advertisements were placed, homoeopathic dispensing establishments attracted a more select clientele.Not surprisingly, professional comment was hostile, and there were scathing references to such treatment and preparations.

More expensive than the remedies readily available from itinerant quacks were patent medicines. There was apparently a touching faith in their government stamp, which was taken as a symbol of authority. Beguiling advertisements appeared for 'Hooping Cough Embrocations', 'Cough and Consumptive Liniments', as well as for drugs which claimed comprehensive powers, like Hopper's Elixir, said to be 'The most Safe, Speedy and Efficacious Cure of Asthmatic and Hooping Coughs, Colds, Hoarseness, Difficulty in Breathings, Consumption, etc.'.[9]

Many products were named to give an illusion of natural remedies. There were Purifying Botanic Pills, Balsam of Coltsfoot and Extract of Bark. Specifically for children there was Pritchett's Vegetable Vermifuge for worms, 'so harmless that it may be taken by an infant an hour old', American Soothing Syrup for teething and the Great American Sarsaparilla 'for the blood' and youthful diseases. Best known of all perhaps were Morison's Vegetable Pills, publicised as a universal panacea on the theory that there was a single cause and a single cure for all disease. There was evidence that overdosing was a cause of child death.[10]

Retail druggists could usually offer cheaper and therefore more popular alternatives. Doctors described them as vying with the gin palaces in their tempting displays and attracting parents who preferred to spend a few pence rather than persevere with the formalities of applying to one of the dispensaries.[11] In 1854 John Leigh, in his evidence as registrar for the Deansgate area of Manchester before the Select Committee on Medical Poor Relief, attributed a quarter of the infant deaths reported to him to advice from 'incompetent and unqualified practitioners'.[12]

Among the agencies of self-help were an increasing number of friendly societies and sick clubs which covered many adult workers, though not their families. Large numbers of factory children were enrolled in Sunday school societies which, like that at Ardwick, typically paid out relief in illness of 1*s* to 2*s* a week and gave a death grant of £2 10*s*.[13] One of the most elaborate in its rules and organisation was the Bury Friendly Society, founded in 1846 with the Rector as president, which accepted members from the age of ten on production of a baptismal certificate. Here a fortnightly payment of $2\frac{1}{2}d$ covered sick allowance and medical attention. Calculated on an actuarial basis members could contribute to a weekly pension of 2*s* in old age.[14]

Quite apart from monetary benefits, Sunday schools had an impact on children's habits. Even the least exclusive were careful to debar those who had 'offensive and contagious distempers'.[15] Thereafter they insisted on standards of cleanliness and tidiness. By their clothing clubs they encouraged thrift and economy and in times of distress they helped children by distributing basic food and clothes.

Observers of the annual Sunday school processions commented approvingly on the children's 'neatness and order' and 'the display of cleanliness, beauty and innocence'.[16] By mid-century the schools were touching the majority of all but the poorest children. In Oldham, for example, on a conservative estimate, about 40 per cent of those between four and fourteen spent some part of the day at Sunday school.[17] A recent investigation of Baptist Sunday school records in the Lancashire towns has referred to their revelation of 'perpetual confrontation with all problems of social deprivation . . .'.[18]

The self-help movement, with its emphasis on discipline, including total abstinence, impinged on children direct and through their parents.[19] At the other extreme there were many children who made early acquaintance with drink. As babies they were plied with gin or rum, 'the finger dipped in the liquor was first given till the taste for it was acquired'.[20] Many infants were insured, by the payment of coppers a week, in more than one public house 'death club'. At death as much as £15 or £16 was paid out, several times the cost of the funeral, which rarely exceeded £3, or, as frequently happened, part of the benefit was given in gin.[21]

Dispensary doctors who were called upon to certify death were under no illusion that it was often both welcome and anticipated. According to a Preston rent collector in 1844, cottagers often informed him 'that they were unable to pay at that time; but when a certain member of the family—generally a child—died, they would be able to pay'. He added, 'I have felt much shocked at this and I have told the people that it was very wrong to depend on anything of the kind . . .'.[22]

Children's general health and prospects of survival depended directly on the family. Caring parents sought help. They not only nursed their children through infections and illness, but on their recovery built them up with 'strengthening medicine', broth, jelly and eggs, and perhaps took them into the country air. It was not only treatment that was important but after-care and exercise. The well-to-do, of course, could provide appropriate nourishment, including beef tea and the means of gentle exercise which indoors was recommended to be taken on the nursery rocking-horse.[23]

Less fortunate children took their chance with illness and accidents and had to survive without the benefits of convalescence. Many, in Engel's words, grew up 'like wild weeds'.[24] Numbers, orphaned or deserted by one or both parents, were obviously disadvantaged. There were others whose parents, according to a dispensary physician, gave up hope too easily in time of distress. When their child was struck with serious illness they were apt to conclude that it had 'received the death stroke and from that moment they cease to seek remedial measures beyond their own resources, quietly awaiting the child's death'.[25]

When the tiny coffin on the kitchen table was a common sight it was hardly surprising that many parents had a fatalistic attitude to death. What outsiders attributed to a blunting of sensitivity was often realistic acceptance of the fact that many who were born would die early. Parents learned to endure. As one observer remarked, it was outsiders, 'people who do not at all know how much they suffered, [who] call them hard-hearted'.[26] Often they made great efforts to get help; amid the frequent references of physicians to the neglect, ignorance and apathy of parents it is possible to glimpse brighter aspects of human nature, the affection and concern of those who sought assistance for their offspring and patiently waited their turn in the crowded dispensary waiting rooms or even in the street outside.

V PHILANTHROPIC ENDEAVOUR

Nationally the later years of the period brought hospital reforms, trained nurses and an emphasis on new architecture to allow maximum air and ventilation. Though town dispensaries in the North-west had extended their work with out-patients, few took in-patients until the late '60s when benefits from the winding up of the Cotton Famine Relief Fund enabled towns like Preston and Blackburn to establish infirmaries. Among the exceptions was the Salford Dispensary, which admitted a few in-patients as early as 1845. The trustees were careful to exclude categories with a high death rate (theoretically children were excluded) and at pains to record in the statistics those patients who were 'dying on entry'. According to the rules, surgical instruments were to be kept 'in a dry receptacle . . . under lock and key'.[1] In Bolton a few surgical cases, as well as others with burns and scalds, were admitted as in-patients from the '40s. By 1855 the provision was extended with the appointment of a new nurse described as 'an intelligent and trustworthy matron'.[2]

While the main transformation in hospital work was to come later, dispensary queues were meanwhile swollen by children of all ages, from infants in arms to young factory workers. They included offspring of the Irish cellar inhabitants who, according to evidence from the Stockport Dispensary, were the most common applicants for relief.[3] All were required to bring 'lines', that is, a subscriber's recommendation, the search for which could mean dangerous delay. Medicine was free but the return of phials and gallipots was required before replenishments could be given. Sometimes little could be done for applicants like the consumptive factory girls at Salford who, when prescribed a period of rest, replied, 'We mun wark, or we shall clem' (starve).[4]

In-patients at the Infirmary (now the Manchester Royal Infirmary) included many from a distance, among them children with a variety of injuries and diseases. Often little girls, so-called child nurses, left at home as baby minders, were brought in with burns and scalds, the result of unguarded fires. Occasionally there was a burnt chimney sweep, like the six-year-old from Bank Top who on 7 April 1840 was admitted with 'Burns of face, neck, chest and arms', and died a few days later.[5] Children were treated for scurvy, particularly during the potato famine. Among girls chorea (St Vitus' Dance) was a common malady. There were also numerous cases of scrofula—swollen glands, diseased joints and bones—as well as rheumatism and abscesses. (Already by 1840 scrofulous sores were being treated by tincture of iodine applied in the form of a poultice with yeast and stale bread.[6]) Some children were reported to be suffering from the 'Effects of Starvation'.

As well as child workers in rope walks, match works and collieries there were many from textiles: tenters, doffers, scavengers, cardsetters and piecers who, as cases of urgency, came with recommendations from local manufacturers and philanthropists from the surrounding towns like Stalybridge, Ashton, Oldham, Colne, Atherton, Bolton, Blackburn and Rochdale. A few died under treatment or were pronounced incurable; among others who became out-patients, some had difficulty in making regular visits and were discharged for non-attendance.

Of child patients at the Infirmary there were numbers who came for amputation after accidents, for cutting for stone and for correction of deformities. In 1840, Martha Whitehead, aged nine, of Dukinfield, was brought in by her father with a wry neck, the result of extensive burns which had been badly treated by an irregular practitioner in the neighbourhood. She presented, it was said, a most frightful spectacle, with the muscles of shoulder and neck so firmly stuck together that they had to be severed.[7] Another report of surgery came in 1846 from a visitor to the Infirmary who recorded his distress at seeing an operaton for stone. 'The subject was a little boy whose eager cry of "Is it done, is it done? Say yes, say yes!" still rings in my ears.'[8] (Instruments were still so primitive that years later a report from the London Children's Hospital referred to the use of a butcher's saw for incision of the knee.[9])

Already the surgical ward had become too small, with patients sometimes two to a bed. Overcrowding of surgical patients added to the dangers of septic poisoning. There were descriptions of horsehair mattresses stained with blood, while cases of hospital gangrene were alluded to as 'soughing sores'.[10] As Florence Nightingale was to assert in 1863 in her *Notes on Hospitals*, 'the most delicate test of sanitary conditions in hospitals is afforded by the progress and termination of surgical cases after operation . . .'.[11]

Visitors were struck by the many young children suffering from deformities. In 1840 there were 124 afflicted with hernia who applied for trusses; and fifty, half of them under four and a half, who applied for leg supports.[12] In fact, according to the surgical instrument maker, most children who required leg supports were under three; their deformity was the result of general disability.[13]

By the same period the Children's Dispensary in Manchester was treating 2,000 patients annually.[14] The waiting room became so crowded that, to avoid squabbles, a system of numbered tickets was introduced. Here too, apart from children suffering from infections and scrofula, there were many cases of deformity. By 1850 the number of spinal diseases was 'far more than would generally be credited'.[15] About five per cent of the patients died but, as the Dispensary committee were at pains to point out, the mortality rate for children under the age of five in the area was 50 per cent. Possibly the institution's low death rate was indicative of the fact that it was mostly parents of the deserving poor who made the effort to bring their children for treatment. Nevertheless, among the waiting crowds there was plenty of evidence of the results of ignorance and neglect as well as of sacrifice and self-denial.

Despite the financial pressures of the '40s the Dispensary survived and in 1853 entered a new era with the appointment of Louis Borchardt, a German refugee, as chief physician. For the next twenty years he was to devote his efforts to expansion, including hospital accommodation.[16] In 1855 the institution was renamed the General Hospital and Dispensary for Sick Children, its objects defined as 'The Medical and Surgical Treatment of Poor Children' and 'The Attainment of Diffusion of Knowledge regarding the Diseases of Children'. The first of a series of petitions for funds was launched in terms intended to appeal to local interests, namely that sick children reduced whole families to paupery and that 'no mills and warehouses can have vigorous men except from strong children'.[17]

The very year following Borchardt's appointment a few beds were made available in the overcrowded dispensary, later described by Oliver Heywood, president of the institution, as 'a dingy, ramshackle old building on the spot where now stands the statue of Prince Albert in front of the Town Hall'.[18] In the tiny ward over sixty patients a year were treated, a mere fraction of the worst cases from the dispensary, children with tuberculous meningitis, inflammation of the lungs, consumption, diseases of the bones and joints, abscesses and ulcers. With so little accommodation available it frequently happened that children died before they could be admitted. As it was, the death rate was of the order of 10 per cent.[19]

Borchardt pressed for more accommodation. The Dispensary was now open daily, with over a hundred children each session in the crowded waiting room. He pointed out in 1857 that, apart from his own institution, there were in the whole of Manchester and Salford, an area where 3,000 children died each year, only sixty beds available for children under fourteen. Many of these were in the Infirmary, where children were treated with adults and were, he considered, exposed to undesirable moral influence; only in separate institutions could children's diseases be given full attention.[20]

Initially, because of the impossibility of segregation, Borchardt had been unable to admit infectious cases. In 1858, however, he was able to set aside a small ward with five beds, the only provision for infectious childhood diseases in the city. With the expansion came regulations on the appointment of nurses. No woman was acceptable who was not able 'to write as well as read with facility'.[21]

By 1868, after twice moving to larger premises, the institution was treating 7,000 patients a year, including 350 in-patients.[22] Many came from the suburbs; others from even farther afield. Already in 1860 the Dispensary (henceforth referred to as the Children's Hospital) had been the first institution in the area to abolish the system of subscribers' recommendations. It had been realised that the system caused delay and suffering, but always its justification had been the safeguard it provided against the abuse of facilities. Dispensaries customarily asked subscribers to make their recommendations available to clergymen and others who could discriminate in favour of the deserving poor. Nevertheless, as Borchardt pointed out, mothers frequently had to spend most of the morning trying to get a recommendation and by the time it had been obtained the dispensary had closed for the day. Many a poor woman had been seen 'drenched to the skin, cold and hungry and weary, who had been all day long rambling from point to point seeking a Recommendation for her sick child'.[23]

Most parents were reluctant to leave their children in the alien atmosphere of a hospital. However, it was the Lying-in Hospital, known after 1855 as St Mary's, which suffered most from parental fears of institutionalisation. The fact was that everywhere lying-in hospitals were associated with contagious puerperal fever and a high death-rate. In the words of a leading article in *The Lancet* in 1861, 'The desolating evil of lying-in hospitals is the aggregation of patients in the same room and in the same building.'[24] Without question, childbirth in isolation was safer.

Because of the dangers associated with congregation St Mary's was unable to fill beds even in its children's ward. Although it extended to ten the age up to which it was prepared to take children, and waived the need for recommendations for in-patients, it was of no avail. Even where patients were of 'tender age' the encouragement to mothers to come and suckle their infants proved unavailing. Meanwhile its services for home confinements were much in demand and, in order to guard against abuses, there was careful scrutiny 'by having every pregnant patient visited and reported on, as to her eligibility, moral, social and pecuniary . . .'.[25]

As charities for childbirth and children the Children's Hospital and St Mary's made a special appeal. The latter, particularly, drew support from women such as Elizabeth Gaskell, who was briefly a member of the Ladies' Committee, and Miss Eleanora Atherton, the Manchester heiress, who visited in her sedan chair. Both were assisted by business and mercantile firms, including members of the German community in Manchester. The names of Birley, Agnew, Philips and Rylands as well as Schwabe, Goldschmidt, Hertz and Reiss occur among many others.[26] Most notable of all among supporters of medical charities was the banking family of Heywood. Benjamin Heywood was an original subscriber to the Children's Dispensary; his son, Oliver, was president of the Children's Hospital and of Salford Infirmary for a quarter of a century.

Practical aid came from Ladies' Committees. Initially, for in-patients at the Children's Hospital, parents were required to provide children with a proper change of linen and to fetch away the soiled linen as often as directed by the matron. For those from homes of 'comfortless poverty' in Salford and Manchester the Ladies' Committee came to the rescue. Members of the committee also visited former patients and gave advice to parents. At Christmas they presented clothing, sometimes frocks and flannel petticoats to the girls and vests and comforters to the boys. They were part of the movement of voluntary endeavour which had called the institution into being in the first place and serviced it with professional skills.

That parents were often opposed to leaving their children in hospital was hardly surprising. It was not only that they found the atmosphere alien; the high death rates associated with urban hospitals everywhere roused their worst fears. As Florence Nightingale herself pointed out, the first requisite of a hospital, 'that it should do the sick no harm', had still to be established.[27] Even caring parents, therefore, might well consider that the chances of recovery were better at home.

However, there was no doubt about the general popularity of out-patients' departments. At the very period in the mid-century when St Mary's was advertising vacant beds for infants, a new institution in Stevenson Square, the Clinical Hospital for the Diseases of Children, later the Clinical Hospital and Dispensary for Children, was besieged by applicants from the neighbourhood of Oldham Road, Rochdale Road, London Road, Ancoats and Piccadilly. In all it served a population of 120,000, densely packed in the cellars and back-to-back houses. Many were Irish, and the great majority were families of labourers, packers and porters as well as factory workers. Queues started early in the morning; women sometimes spent the night with their children in the street in order to have a better chance when the doors were opened, and each day would-be patients were turned away. The death rate of infant and child patients was usually 10 per cent, depending on the seasonal prevalence of disease. Among them, those in the most lamentable condition and the earliest to succumb were the illegitimate offspring of the Irish.[28]

By 1861 the hospital had two beds for use in emergency and in 1865, after its move to Cheetham Hill Road, twenty-four. The crowded area of the new site was described in the report of 1870. 'It is doubtful if a similar aggregation of poor people can be found elsewhere in this kingdom, not excepting London. An evening stroll through some of these districts . . . would serve to astonish many who think themselves already acquainted with most of the phases of human character.'[29] As in the case of the Children's Hospital, Continental influence was strong both professionally in the person of the Hungarian refugee Dr Merei, co-founder, who established the Clinical Hospital as a research and training school for the Department of Medical Science, and financially in support from members of the business community.

The very helplessness of the young made their cause unique. Even in a commercially-minded age the needs of children roused social sympathy which found practical expression in a variety of ways. At the local level there were charitable organisations which helped children directly by taking them in from the streets or providing for their welfare in nurseries and schools; there were others which helped them indirectly by encouraging in parents habits of thrift and cleanliness.

For children of the lowest strata, part of the social chasm of urban life, there were Ragged Schools. From the mid-century such schools came into existence in Manchester, Salford, Stockport, Bolton, Bury and Macclesfield. The largest took in several hundred outcasts, first on a daily basis from 7 a.m. and sometimes later as residents. Many as orphans were living rough; others were beggars or rag pickers. On entry they were washed, clothed and fed. Regular simple meals were provided, and over a period children were trained in some trade or craft.

Many suffered from diseases of poverty which affected particularly the eyes and skin. Sometimes during prevalence of skin disease in residential institutions an alteration of diet would be introduced—an allowance of coffee and bread alternately with the usual oatmeal porridge.[30] The children were also prone to infections and the occasional one to epileptic fits for which, as at the Stockport school, the treatment was a hot bath. The trouble was that a large bath 'could not be got ready under five or six hours'.[31] By a regime of cleanliness and industry and by rigorous moral training volunteers sought to transform children. The conflict was 'that of civilisation against barbarism, knowledge against ignorance, virtue against vice and social elevation against degradation'.[32] As an encouragement to subscribers children were assembled and displayed at the annual meetings. As with charity school children of the previous century, it was 'virtue rendered visible'.

Intended especially for infants of working mothers, there were by 1870 three day nurseries in Manchester and Salford established by volunteers. Here babies as young as two weeks could be left from 5 a.m. until 6 or 7 p.m. In particular, the Salford Greengate Nursery accomplished wonders. They came 'very puny children, and scabby and dirty, and in a month you would not know them, the change is so marvellous'.[33]

One of the Manchester nurseries was founded in 1869 by a surgeon at St Mary's and maintained largely by private donations. He described the condition of the infants, nearly all of whom were brought infested with fleas and lice.[34] On arrival they were stripped, washed and had their hair combed with a fine-tooth comb. Some were so infested that their clothing was burnt. The next day they would be back in the same condition. Despite the low charge of 4*d* a day mothers preferred to make their own private arrangements with women they knew. Often factory workers or washerwomen might pay three or four shillings a week, a large part of their earnings, for an infant to be fed on 'pobbies' or arrowroot and water. Such children were said to be continually vermin-ridden. The founder of the nursery attributed the mothers' attitude to 'pre-conceived prejudice against charity'. More probably they disliked interference 'from above' and the imposition of standards which entailed an uncomfortable change of habits.

For similar reasons they sometimes avoided sending older children to the grant-aided day schools associated with the Churches. They objected to the fixed hours, the rules about sending children with clean clothes and short, tidy hair.[35] Instead they chose to patronise dame schools, often no more than child-minding establishments, because they could send children when they pleased. Unlike the elementary school authorities, the dames asked no awkward questions and never pursued absentees.

However, because of the efforts of churchmen at local and national level the number of Church schools grew. Many were largely infant schools and simply provided a place of safety for young children. They were kept out of mischief while the mothers worked or looked after subsequent offspring. Indeed, it was said of the young attenders that 'some [were] scarcely able to walk'.[36] Exceptionally there was by the '60s in Manchester an organisation, the Education Aid Society, which not only contributed towards the cost of schooling for poor children but also in two city schools provided school dinners at a cost of $4\frac{3}{4}d$ a week, $1d$ of which was required from the parents.[37] One of the promoters of the society explained the long-term objectives which might be achieved by education. He pointed out that the high infant and child death rate was not primarily due to poverty or lack of food or drink. It was 'from want of ideas, want of moral and industrial training, want of the power of thinking, want of cleanliness, want of order, want of fit residences, want of sympathy between class and class'.[38]

Outstanding among voluntary groups for the scale of its activity and its professional expertise was the Manchester and Salford Sanitary Association, established in 1852 with the objective of spreading knowledge of the laws of health and of promoting temperance.[39] Chief among the founders was Thomas Turner, who as surgeon of the

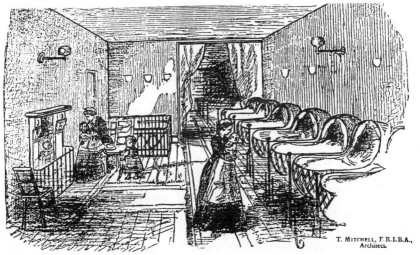

T. MITCHELL, F.R.I.B.A.,
Architect.

Type of day nursery favoured by the Manchester and Salford Sanitary Association for women factory workers' infants and young children

Manchester Royal Infirmary had seen many infants wasting away as a result of ignorance and neglect. By meetings and publications the association sought to make an impact on public opinion. Through its members, physicians associated with Poor Law Unions, voluntary hospitals and gaols, it was able to draw up and publish weekly returns of cases of disease so that epidemics could be quickly spotted and brought under control. By lectures and by the distribution of leaflets it sought to promote sanitary knowledge. From the '60s the association was pressing for more fever beds, especially for isolating children with scarlet fever.

Meanwhile the Ladies' Sanitary Reform Association, founded in 1862 and later to become the Ladies' Health Society of Manchester and Salford, took charge of clothing and blanket clubs and arranged lectures on artisan cookery. The system of home visiting which the society organised was a successful innovation and more effective than health lectures or the distribution of tracts. For the purpose the ladies engaged specially-trained women and paid for their services while they themselves acted as superintendents. The former were in fact early health visitors, who gave advice on infant feeding and who distributed and demonstrated the use of disinfectant in notorious areas like Angel Meadow.

In a variety of ways charitable organisations sought to assist children themselves or to influence parental upbringing. Sometimes, as in the case of medical charities, their help was invoked; at other times, as with the provision of nurseries, it was resented as patronage or as an inconvenient impingement on daily life.

VI PUBLIC PROVISION

Direct public responsibility for children was confined to the offspring of paupers through Boards of Guardians. Otherwise with the exception of vaccination, for which there were ever stronger measures of compulsion, child welfare was considered the personal concern of the parent. The private relationship between parent and child was held to be inviolable; intervention would undermine individual obligations.

Hence for compulsory education of factory children it was the employers who were held responsible. Thus factory children in the area were the first of a series of special categories to be protected by legislation.[1] Under the Factory Act of 1833 children between the ages of nine and thirteen were allowed to work as short-timers, with an eight-hour day, on condition they attended school two hours daily. From 1844 the famous half-time system actually allowed children to commence work at eight but restricted working hours until the age of thirteen to six and a half or seven each day, and required them to attend school daily for a single session. Legislation was primarily a security against overwork. In the early years when children were crammed into dames' cellars and factory coal-holes, or crowded on backless benches in elementary schools, they may well have been more confined and in less wholesome surroundings than at their labours. Those who had come straight from the heated mills shivered with cold in damp, sunless schoolrooms.[2]

Employers connived with parents to elude detection. Proof of a child's age was a major difficulty in the days before the registration of births, and sometimes local factory surgeons were constrained to use a tooth test to ascertain age. There were, however, many abuses, and factory inspectors, who in the process of investigation were 'in constant motion from town to town and station to station', noted the diminutive size of children.[3] In fact the early inspectors and their assistants undertook the duties of factory police. On their surprise visits they discovered children hidden away, secreted under baskets or behind trap-doors.[4]

Even in the late '50s, a quarter of a century after the first major legislation, there were advertisements couched in such terms as 'Wanted from twelve to twenty boys, not younger than will pass for thirteen years of age . . .'.[5] Eventually, however, the half-time system found acceptance. Factory surgeons not only rejected applicants on grounds of age; as a result of examination, they often deferred entry to work until children had received vaccination or had been treated for defective conditions such as scrofula, scald-head and skin diseases.

Nevertheless it is doubtful whether the system was as advantageous on health grounds as had been intended. For example, Leonard Horner, the local factory inspector, had enthusiastically supported it in the belief that it would give children plenty of time in the open air and opportunities for play, and he had expected that they would

Surgeon's certificate issued under the 1844 Factory Act. This particular certificate permits entry to full-time work. From Charles Brown, *Sixty-four Years a Doctor*, Preston, 1922

No. 396.   [COPY]

FACTORIES REGULATION ACT, 7 Vic. c. 15.
Certificate of Age of a Young Person
To be employed in the factory of Messrs. W. Calvert & Sons, situated in Walton-le-Dale.

I, Robert Charles Brown, of Preston, duly appointed a Certifying Surgeon, do hereby certify That *Margaret Eccles, Dr.* of *James Eccles* and *Dorothy Eccles*, residing in *Walton-le-Dale*, has been personally examined by me, this *Second* day of *December*, One thousand eight hundred and sixty-three ; and that the said Young Person has the ordinary Strength and Appearance of a Young Person of at least THIRTEEN YEARS of Age, and that I believe the real Age of the said Young Person to be at least Thirteen Years ; and that the said Young person is not incapacitated, by Disease or bodily Infirmity, from working daily in the above-named Factory for the time allowed by this Act.

(Signed)   ROBERT CHARLES BROWN,
Certifying Surgeon.

change their clothes and wash between work and school.[6] The reality was very different, with children coming to school covered in fluff, grease and dirt. Many were disorderly and inattentive, others—usually the afternoon half-timers—so stupid with drowsiness that their faculties were benumbed.[7] In the larger centres there were complaints that the legislation could be frustrated by children changing jobs so frequently that the inspector rarely caught up with them.[8]

Over the years, however, it became more difficult to evade regulations. Gradually insistence by teachers on neatness and cleanliness had its effect on appearance and health. Older workers viewed with wistful envy the easier initiation of the half-timers compared with their own harsh introduction to the factory regime.[9] Within the area observers noted that in other trades children were employed longer hours and often in more laborious work. In the long term the ethos, discipline and content of schooling was designed to mould character, to tame a rough population and to inculcate the virtues of moderation, thrift and self-control which would reflect on both the health and the morals of the next generation. Horner laid stress on training children to early habits of industry and submission to authority, and saw the half-time system 'elevating the moral and social condition of the humbler classes'. Thus for factory children education was considered as necessary as vaccination: each was for the direct protection of society, the one against moral and the other against physical disease.[10]

By law, following the smallpox epidemic of 1837–41, vaccination was to be provided free by Boards of Guardians. In fact practice varied. Where, in densely populated areas, Poor Law surgeons were well paid for each vaccination they had every incentive to seek out infants. In the Manchester Union, which paid 1*s* 6*d* a head, medical officers had a profitable private arrangement by which they employed men to check registered births and paid twopence for every child brought to them.[11] Thus costs for vaccination in the Manchester Union township—£41 14*s* in a single quarter of 1846—were the highest in the locality.[12] Similarly in Preston one of the surgeons on his own initiative went round to homes where he vaccinated between 400 and 500 infants a year, sometimes despite parental objections.[13]

By implication there was evidently some resistance to vaccination in the area. In Stockport, for example, it was reported that parents were readier to agree when it was an arm-to-arm operation from a child of their own choice.[14] Here, however, since the economy-minded Guardians paid only sixpence for each vaccination, there was little incentive for surgeons to seek out new births. Even after the stricter legislation of the mid-century many Boards of Guardians were dilatory about carrying out their obligation or, when they provided vaccination, made no effort to enforce it. (Thus in some districts the old system of inoculation persisted into the '40s.)[15] Parents could make their own arrangements if they chose, and sometimes had children vaccinated by midwives or druggists. Since no qualification was required till 1860 '. . . all persons . . . clergymen, amateurs, druggists, old women . . . etc.' were allowed to vaccinate. The result was that in the early 'sixties about half the infants were vaccinated but relatively few were 'well vaccinated'.[16]

The association of vaccination with the Poor Law in the public mind was unfortunate. The workhouse and the pauper's grave roused fear in respectable families. Few adults had not experienced acute poverty or could feel wholly confident of meeting expenses of sudden death. Hence babies at birth were entered in 'burying clubs' and subscriptions (sometimes as low as a penny a month) were maintained even in times of hardship to avoid the degradation of a pauper funeral.

The full imposition of the 1834 Poor Law was resisted in the textile areas, and all sorts of anomalies survived before the building of large new 'Unions'. In general, so strong was local feeling that outdoor relief persisted for many years. The threat, however, of the Stockport Guardians in 1840 to withdraw such relief and instead take children of large families into the workhouse school had an immediate effect in checking 'the inordinate desire for outdoor relief'.[17] Starvation was preferable to the 'House'.

During periods of distress, relief was on a large scale. In 1848 it was estimated that 60,000 children were relieved by Lancashire Unions;[18] some fifteen years later, during the cotton famine, there were individual Unions which were each giving outdoor relief to 5,000 or more children. However, the weekly relief, usually of the order of 6*d* to 1*s* a head, kept a child alive and little more. It led to low vitality and often future disability or enfeeblement.

For some time little in the way of medical help was provided by Poor Law Guardians. It was reported of the Burnley workhouse in 1844 that there was no provision for childbirth; a pauper woman was simply given 2*s* and sent to 'an ignorant midwife'.[19] Even when Unions had appointed medical officers, rates of pay (which also included the provision of medicine) were scarcely sufficient to cover adequate treatment. As late as 1863 the average fee paid to one Preston officer for each outdoor case, including midwifery, was 5*d*. It was little wonder that the Guardians were accused of letting out 'the lives of their poor fellow creatures upon contract in a manner similar to the way in which people let out so many thousand shoes to make'.[20] Nor was it surprising that people had little confidence in parish doctors and their drugs. Whenever possible poor families preferred to seek assistance from dispensaries, where they felt they received better attention and superior medicine. There were many, however, who could not reach a dispensary and whose children were lost for lack of medical aid.

Though in due course the new workhouses made provision for the destitute sick in infirmaries, these were identified with the socially outcast and were accordingly shunned. There were lying-in wards where a large proportion of births were illegitimate and where the death rate of such unfortunate infants was high. So great was the stigma attached to birth in a workhouse that there were families who pawned all they had to avoid such an event. One woman was even known to have given birth to a child on the bare floor of her home rather than go to the 'House'.[21] There were sordid disputes between Unions over the maintenance of orphans and illegitimate offspring which led to children being dragged backwards and forwards between Union boundaries. There was even a case of Guardians refusing the cost of an infant coffin. Elsewhere an officious relieving officer tried to bully parents into a cemetery funeral for their child by refusing to pay fees for a churchyard burial. He gave way only when, with the child still unburied, the father prepared to beg in the streets for the money.[22]

Of the children who found their way into the workhouses many were orphaned or deserted; others were the offspring of vagrants and were taken in between their seasonal excursions into the outer world. Customarily an 'able-bodied' boy broke stones for three and a half hours a day for his keep, while 'able-bodied' girls, like the women, helped with the washing. The older unreformed workhouses were often crowded and dirty. Children were mixed with idiots and with the ordinary inmates. They had no playground and at night slept with adults or were put together five or six to a bed. From a number of workhouses children were sent to work daily in the factories.[23]

In times of distress there was severe overcrowding and in the early '40s even a new workhouse had to pack over a hundred children by night and by day into rooms only 39 ft by 21 ft.[24] Initially there was no classification of the sick wards except by sex, so that young and old, able-bodied and decrepit were put together. An investigator in Stockport in the late '60s noted the close proximity in the same ward of cases of scabies and venereal disease as well as infirmity from old age. Among the patients was 'a boy of tender years'.[25] Purpose-built institutions, however, were required to have infirmaries equipped with separate wards for infectious diseases. There were stern warnings when Poor Law inspectors found infectious cases in ordinary wards; following an unfavourable report on the new Bolton workhouse in 1864, additional wings were added to provide isolation facilities.[26] Though isolation was evaded for most childhood infections, it became

generally accepted for cases of smallpox. Indeed, so numerous were
infectious patients in some Union hospitals that they were regarded as
fever hospitals.

Commonly workhouse children suffered from infested heads and
from scabies, known as 'the itch'. Even the old institutions were
compelled to set up boys' itch wards (girls were usually put in with
the women) and sore-head wards.[27] Of the head diseases, ringworm,
associated with fungous growth to the roots of the hair and scald-
head, where the scalp was encrusted with sores and scabs, were the
hardest to eradicate.[28] Often too children had scrofulous glands and
inflammation of the eyes. 'Sore eyes', the result of malnutrition, was
the particular mark of the workhouse child, whose eyelids were often
covered with scabs and scales. The condition was highly infectious
and was treated, certainly up to the middle years of the century, by
putting leeches on the temple as well as by ointment. Isolation on a
low diet was then recommended.[29] Perhaps the Preston Guardians
were both enlightened and generous when in 1859 they decided that
the best form of cure would be to cut the children's hair and give them
a day trip to the seaside.[40]

In contrast, many Guardians, through lack of supervision or
insistence on economy, were responsible for much child suffering and
even death. The practice of using inmates, including imbeciles, to look
after the children was fraught with peril. In 1868 one infant in a
Wigan workhouse was scalded to death by an idiot nurse who plunged
it into a bucket of hot water. According to the reports 'the body
presented a most shocking appearance, with skin hanging off in
strips'. It transpired that of the 'nurses' in the infant ward, two were
'not right', a third was half paralysed and the others were over eighty
years old.[31] An investigation of a recently built Rochdale workhouse
two years later revealed appalling conditions. Forty children were in
cramped quarters which 'reeked of sulphur and impurity'. Despite
doses of brimstone and treacle and cod-liver oil they looked pale and
ill, and many were covered in scabs from head to foot. It was
discovered that their food was frequently sour, with the leavings of
Thursday's 'lobby' put into Friday's pie, and Friday's leavings again
saved for Monday's 'lobby'.[32]

Whenever large numbers of pauper children were together it was
assumed that there would be a high incidence of infection. When the

Manchester Union built its School of Industry at Swinton in 1842 for 1,300 pauper children, it made provision for 20 per cent of inmates in infirmary wards. There were separate fever wards, foul wards and scald-head wards, each designed to have its own airing-ground, separate from the yard for the convalescent sick. Special rooms were set aside as 'coffin store' and 'dead house'.[33]

A generous diet at Swinton was justified on the grounds that children were engaged in physical work. Each child had meat four days a week for dinner, rice milk and pease soup on the other days, with a pint of milk and porridge for breakfast and another pint of milk with six ounces of bread for supper.[34] (By contrast, of course, the fare of many children at home—potatoes and a little bacon, bread-and-treacle and tea—was much inferior in quantity and quality). Even so the sickness rate often exceeded the proportions anticipated in 1842, and almost a third of the children were listed as sick in weekly returns.[35]

Many of the children at Swinton had come from the underworld. Some were so crippled and weak that they would not survive. Others were potential members of the so-called dangerous classes in society. It was recognition at national level of the threat posed by incipient criminals that led to the extension in the provision of Industrial Schools. Thus State assistance became available to expand and regularise the work of local voluntary bodies. Hence, as at Stockport, the Ragged School was transformed in 1866 into a larger Industrial School with emphasis on training for physical, mental and moral fitness.[36] The weekly bath, hot or cold, according to season, the close cropping of hair and regular skin examination were basic parts of a regime which sought to inculcate the spirit of industry and self-respect.

From the late '30s and early '40s, years of distress associated with disorder and violence, tensions had eased. Even the agonising period of the cotton famine was, in Kay Shuttleworth's phrase, 'endured without a murmur'.[37] Twenty years before, many who had defied authority were first-generation factory workers, rootless and resentful of discipline, which they felt to be unnatural and degrading. In the meantime self-help movements and schooling as well as years of prosperity had helped the process of adjustment.

Within the towns efforts had been made to improve conditions. Though progress was uneven, there were advances in sanitation, sewerage and street paving. Manchester led the way in providing a good water supply. From the middle years of the century authorities were setting up public baths and wash-houses. (Bury, however, excluded the latter on the grounds that they would take women from their homes.)[38] Even the disastrous years of the cotton famine brought improvements, since labour was mobilised in public works, including drainage and sewering in unhealthy districts and the paving of roads. Gradually, as towns became incorporated, they assumed responsibility for water and for the establishment of parks. For many households, however, the installation of piped water lay in the future, while for all but the most fortunate children the only playground was the crowded street, almost as dangerous as the factory for accidents.

THREE

THE FACTORY AGE,
1870–1900

I CHILDREN AND INDUSTRY

The high Victorian period lies midway between the early years of power-driven machinery and our own era. Recollections from former operatives, or at second hand through their children, bring a sense of intimacy. While silk employees clung on in the hope of better times, cotton workers took confidence in an expanding industry. It was a period of new mill building, larger units more highly powered, with machinery designed to run faster, and of growing specialisation between weaving in the north and spinning in the south. The processes were familiar to all—willowing, scutching, carding, roving, mule or ring spinning, winding, weaving and finishing. The future seemed secure, and. among prosperous artisans were some who invested their savings in the new public companies.

In general the '80s and '90s were boom years for cotton. Because the manufacturing process was particularly labour-intensive, the most conspicuous population increases were recorded in the northern weaving towns. It was here that more and more half-timers were recruited.[1] So great was the demand for their labour that a father who had several children of appropriate age would be given a job in preference to other applicants.[2] For many families the system was a way of life, and former half-timers survive today with vivid memories of the past.

Gradually social disciplines were imposed to restrain the worst aspects of industrialism. There were public health measures, as well as measures for compulsory education with the extension of years of schooling for earlier conscript categories. The conclusion of the century was to bring a greater realisation in human terms of the scale of physical deterioration and of the need for positive action on behalf of the young.

In 1873 the economic loss from high infant and child mortality was publicised in the Registrar General's report; Farr computed that at birth each individual was worth £5, by the age of five £56, and by fifteen £192.[3] Significantly the birth rate began to fall. Through the greater part of the century, by a combination of natural increase and in-migration, the population of the towns had risen without check. When the national birth rate was at its peak at 36 per 1,000 of the population in 1876, the rates in the textile towns were well ahead: 49 in Stockport and Burnley, 47 in Oldham, 45 in Blackburn and 42 in Preston. From that point there was a decline, though the incidence was uneven between towns. Within twenty years the birth rate in Blackburn had dropped by almost a third (to 31); within a quarter of a century by two-fifths (to 26). Even Preston, where the change was barely perceptible in the '80s, saw a dramatic decline to 30 per 1,000 by the turn of the century. By then several of the textile towns were recording birth rates under the national average, 29 per 1,000.[4]

In part children had become less profitable as the years of dependence had increased; in part the lower birth rate reflected a decline of in-migration, since most earlier arrivals had come at a youthful age. Even in the decade of the '70s gains by in-migration in Blackburn, for example, contributed only 6 per cent to total population increase, down to 21 per cent compared with 36 per cent in the decade of the '50s. By the '80s they contributed less than 3 per cent to a total increase of 15 per cent.[5] Excessive infantile mortality had long been associated with the progressive degeneration of mothers under conditions of town life. The extent of physical deterioration was thus seen to be related to the number of generations who had lived in urban areas, a direct consequence of social heredity. Without the injection of new stock on the scale of the past the prospects were of accelerating deterioration.

Meanwhile the number of half-timers increased. By 1875 there were 67,000 in the cotton industry, accounting for 14 per cent of all employees. Fifteen years later there were almost 90,000, half the total number in the whole country.[6] Gradually protection was extended, but each advance in the minimum age for part-time work to nine, ten, eleven and eventually twelve was resisted by parents and employers

County Borough  of Bury.
Holt, Mayor.

CONDITIONS
UPON WHICH
CHILDREN are entitled to WORK HALF-TIME and FULL-TIME.

HALF-TIME.

A Child of 12 YEARS OF AGE is entitled to a Certificate TO WORK HALF-TIME:

1,—If such child has attended 300 TIMES IN EACH YEAR in not more than 2 Schools for 5 years, whether consecutive or not,

OR

2.—If such child has passed the 3rd STANDARD (Labour Examination) and would IN THE OPINION OF THE COMMITTEE BE NECESSARILY AND BENE-FICIALLY EMPLOYED.

FULL-TIME.

A child BETWEEN 13 AND 14 YEARS OF AGE is entitled to a Certificate TO WORK FULL-TIME:

1.—If such child has attended 350 TIMES IN EACH YEAR in not more than 2 Schools for 5 years, whether consecutive or not,

OR

2.—If such child has passed the 5th STANDARD (Labour Examination).

JOHN HASLAM,

Corporation Offices, Bank Street, Bury,   Clerk to the School
31st December, 1900.   Attendance Committee.

Charles Vickerman & Sons, Printers, Bookbinders, &c., 19, Union Square, Bury.

Handbill publicising for the benefit of parents and employers the conditions of the new legislation for employment of children in 1901 alike. In 1875 there were protests from Rochdale that the proposed increase from nine to ten would eliminate a quarter of the half-timers, about 1,000 children.[7] At the same period the 5,000 half-timers in Oldham numbered a third of the total school rolls, and almost a half of average attenders.[8] Of all the towns Blackburn had the highest numbers, almost 6,000.[9] Some parents found ways of evading the regulations. As one factory inspector reported, 'On my upbraiding a parent for sending her boy at $12\frac{1}{2}$ to work full-time, she replied, "Aw didn't know aw was duin wrang, th' lad's a good scholar, aw suppose aw mun send him t'pit if you wunnot leet him wark abuv ground".'[10]

Certain branches of industry came to shed half-timers. For example, with the disappearance of small firms of calico printers in districts of the north and north-east there was no longer need of child 'teerers' and dyehouse boys. However, the new concentration of weaving in the area increased the demand for young tenters. Overall, by the early '90s one child in every two of the appropriate age group in Lancashire was said to be a half-timer.[11] In the textile areas the vast majority were in the mills: smaller numbers went as shop assistants, errand boys, laundry girls and the like. In towns such as Chorley half-time certificates reached record figures in the mid-'90s.[12] It was in the weaving towns, too, that proposals to increase the minimum age of half-timers to twelve (which came into effect in 1901) were most strongly resisted. Parents and employers alike voiced their opposition, while municipal officials brought pressure to bear on parliamentary representatives and publicly extolled the virtues of the half-time system. The typical middle-class view, publicly expressed by a dignitary (and former mayor) of Burnley, was that it was impossible to 'imagine a more healthy and reasonable mode of bringing up a child than in occupying him in some practical and useful work for one half of the day and engaging him for the other half in study'.[13]

The necessity of reaching the respective standards fixed as the conditions of half-time exemption and for school-leaving provided an educational incentive for children and parents alike. With large families to keep, the commencement of work by older offspring, paid as half-timers at up to three shillings a week and at least double that rate as full-timers, was eagerly awaited. Hence there were strong pressures on children to pass the required examinations at the appropriate stages. In his own home, as George Tomlinson recollected forty years later, the 2s 3d which he earned as a half-timer in a Rishton factory was a necessity in the parental budget.[14] Factory surgeons reported cases of tampering with birth certificates so that children could go to work prematurely. Some attempts at falsification were obviously crude, but occasionally the birth certificate of an older sibling who had died was substituted.[15] When questioned on age, children were well drilled to respond appropriately with their 'factory age'![16]

Medical investigation revealed significant defects in the physique of urban factory children compared with rural children of similar age. It also revealed differences between factory children in the towns and those in smaller communities accessible to the countryside. Almost universally flea-bitten, urban children suffered to a much greater extent from rickets and flat feet.[17] Factory surgeons looked for vaccination marks and sent unvaccinated children to the proper authorities. Similarly, where they noticed conditions in need of treatment, such as scabies and ringworm, they were known to refuse certificates for employment and send children to dispensaries.[18]

Whether in town or village the labour of the child textile worker was probably more intensive than in most trades. Accidents were still common. In bleachworks, for example, there were instances of boys falling into the boiling liquid in the keirs.[19] Of factory injuries, records such as those of Quarry Bank Mill include a number of references to laceration and loss of a limb. For instance, on 23 January 1889 a boy in the mule room narrowly escaped death when his head was caught between the carriage and the roller beam. 'The upper part of one ear was cut off and a severe scalp wound inflicted.'[20] Some forty years after legislation had prohibited the cleaning of moving machinery by young workers there were serious accidents, some of them fatal, from just such a cause. Hospitals reported cases of children so badly mangled by machinery that they died. The list of deaths at the Rochdale Infirmary in 1880, for example, included 'A boy aged twelve who was caught by a strap and dragged into the engine suffered from severe compound fracture of the legs and thigh. Immediate amputation of the hip was required. The patient sank within three hours.'[21]

Former half-timers who had worked as piecers in spinning factories recollected their fear of being caught in the machinery whenever they slipped on the oily wooden floors. They recalled the constant pain from splinters in their bare feet and their exhaustion from keeping pace with the mules for six hours a day as well as covering the distances from home to work and back—often several miles—followed by a stint of schooling.[22] As tenters in the weaving sheds half-timers were kept busy refilling the shuttles and fetching supplies of weft as they were needed. At the end of the week looms had to be swept and alleys left clean. Sometimes they were conscious of the discomfort and strain: the 'factory fever', brought on by itch from the cotton which affected them as beginners and the difficulty of working by gaslight on dark mornings and picking up the broken ends on the looms.[23]

Teachers noted the 'great physical change' which came over children as soon as they became half-timers. As one Oldham headmaster reported to the Cross Commission in 1887, the half-timer 'suddenly seems to change his nature altogether, for whereas before he might be a bright intelligent child, now he has become, I was going to say dull—it does in some measure come to that'.[24] Others spoke of half-timers being overpressed and falling asleep at their lessons. Child labour was denounced by the National Union of Teachers. As a spokesman pointed out in 1897, workers in the town of Oldham alone put away £200,000 for the annual 'wakes' week, yet they sent their eleven-year-olds into the mills to help to earn it. Of the children he said, 'In England we kill them by inches.'[25] Youngsters themselves were well aware that teachers took less interest in them once they became half-timers, presumably because so little could be expected of them.

Doctors were explicit on the adverse effects of premature entry to work and noted the frequency of skin disease and defective eyesight. There were new dangers, the result of such innovations as the heavy sizing (with compounds of china clay and flour) of the cotton yarn which filled the weaving sheds with dust and over a period affected the lungs of the girl tenters and of the weavers. Both were also prone to phthisis by reason of tubercle infection from shuttle threading, a process by which they sucked thread through the shuttle many times a day. A former Bolton tenter described how distasteful she had found 'shuttle kissing'. She noted that most weavers had bad teeth, 'aggravated by the constant suction'. Many had false teeth before they were twenty.[26]

Two young weavers in Bolton at the end of the nineteenth century. Note the clogs, shawl hanging on the wall under the stylish hat and, alongside, shuttles, and also the gas lighting.

Medical reports stressed the long-term effects of work on children's mental development and on their physical powers of resistance to disease. Though the qualifying age for half-time work was raised by stages to twelve by the turn of the century, once the children entered the factory physical development was stunted. In the twentieth century between the wars one of the Medical Officers of Health in Rochdale recorded the average increase in heights and weights of contemporary twelve- to thirteen-year-olds and compared them with those recorded of the half-timers of similar age a generation before (see table below). Though the earlier statistics relate to 1908 (and cover, incidentally, the three-quarters of Rochdale twelve-year-olds who became half-timers), the contrast was startling. Had they existed, nineteenth-century figures for the same age-group would have shown an even greater discrepancy. With the transition to full-time work of fifty-five hours a week at thirteen the adolescent, as the medical officer of 1908 noted, 'elongates slightly in time, but remains very thin, loses colour, the muscles remain small . . . the legs are inclined to become bowed . . . the arch of the foot flattens and the teeth decay rapidly'.[27]

Comparison of average weight and height of half-timers (1908) and schoolchildren (1932) in Rochdale[28]

| | | | | *Yearly increase* | |
Year	Age 5	Age 12	Age 13	Age 5–12	Age 12–13
		Weight (kg)			
1908	16·7	30·6	32·8	2·0	2·2
1932	16·7	30·9	35·8	2·0	4·9
		Height (cm)			
1908	101·8	134·4	138·0	4·7	3·6
1932	104·9	137·9	145·3	4·7	7·4

Compared with children in small-scale industries, however, those in the textile factories were distinctly better off. Despite the discomforts and the hazards factories were healthier than workshops or homes where domestic trades were carried on. In 1876 even the youngest half-timer was better off than children in neighbouring Cheshire saltworks who from the age of four were breaking up tubs of dried salt and 'smashing it up with axes and things'.[29] From farther afield one of the factory inspectors compared the 'dreary labour holes' in Birmingham with the large well ventilated factories of the North-west and commented that it was 'no wonder that a different spirit seems ... to animate the Lancashire and Birmingham operative'.[30] For the former there had been a long tradition of protection both as child and as juvenile worker, and a similarly long tradition of part-time schooling; for the latter, protection came some thirty years later and even then was less comprehensive.

II CHILDREN AND THE ENVIRONMENT

The period was to bring a determined onslaught on defective drainage and sanitation and an attempt to alert ordinary householders to health risks. As the medical officer for Bolton wrote in 1873, 'Medicine cures individuals but Hygiene saves whole communities.' So long as people were allowed to squat in the appalling conditions of the town's alleys and courts 'the Dispensary may send its officers, the various benevolent societies may bestow their alms, and the Poor Law Guardians may administer outdoor relief to the dwellers in those dismal places without any permanent advantage to the recipients ...'.[1]

The problems were enormous. Each town had its notorious areas, often those with a large proportion of Irish settlers. In Ashton it was Botany, where, according to the medical officer, the ashpits were overflowing and closets in such filthy condition that it was 'unfit for pedestrians to pass along';[2] in Wigan it was Scholes, with its dank alleys and decayed houses; in Rochdale it was Wardleworth; in Bury, East ward; in Bolton, Bradford ward; in Salford, Regent Road and Greengate, including the infamous Birtle's Square. In Oldham the worst homes (in Westwood and St Mary's) were said to emit a putrid smell like that of typhus fever. According to the medical officer, 'If it were not for the porous brick walls human beings could not continue to live in these places.'[3] In Manchester Deansgate, including Dyer's Court and Cupid's Alley, together with St George's and Ancoats, were the worst areas. Of houses in Ancoats the Manchester medical officer wrote:

Let anyone accustomed to better conditions of life put his head into one of them, and he will be met with a mephitic atmosphere the like of which is not to be found in the domicile of any other animal. Stables and shippons, and even pigstyes, have their peculiar smells, but they are not poisonous, or repulsive, or offensive as these. No animal could live in them and flourish.[4]

Children, like plants, withered in an atmosphere polluted by sewage, smoke and the smell of gasworks, tripe boiling, brick-making and the like. Already airborne particles from the Manchester atmosphere had been examined with the aid of a new precision microscope and reported to contain 'fungoid matter'.[5] With advances in medical knowledge it was now recognised that disease was caused by germs in the air, in water and in food. Attention was focused on the almost universal privy midden system, subsequently described by the Chief Medical Officer of the Local Government Board as 'degrading and ignoble as it is foul'.[6]

As a consequence of the filth—and in many towns the privy middens persisted well into the twentieth century—the infantile mortality rate, the so-called hygienic barometer, remained high throughout the latter years of the century. With the degree of public squalor many urban families were discouraged from making an effort and simply lived in conditions of habitual dirt. Indeed, dirt was almost impossible to eradicate. It came, as did infection, with the garments they retrieved from the pawnshop. It came in their furniture, from the cheap upholstery stuffed with dirty rags and flocks taken from household rubbish, middens and tips.[7] It came even on the money they handled.

Teachers had often taken for granted the stench of unwashed bodies and discharging ears. With girls in particular, infested heads were almost universal. The lice simply dropped from their hair on to the desks. Dirt bred disease. There were children who, as a result of uncleanliness, had bleeding ringworm of the scalp, skin diseases, swollen and inflamed glands. Poor vision, running noses and sore mouths were commonplace.[8]

When in the early years of the twentieth century schoolchildren were first medically examined the worst conditions of uncleanliness and neglect came from the factory districts of the North-west. Often more than half the children examined were dirty. It was easier for feckless parents to escape detection in the anonymity of urban life and avoid the pressures of public opinion which were brought to bear in smaller localities and closely knit communities. The mill towns recorded the highest proportions of verminous children and of those who were inadequately clothed and shod.[9] There were always children who had their clothes sewn on. In the summer many came barefoot to school; in the winter, if they were lucky, clogs might be provided from a voluntary fund.

Parental attitudes, revealed at the time of the early examinations, from 1909 onwards, reflected long-held customs and inhibitions. The mothers, who themselves were reared in the '70s and '80s, drew on their own experience as children. Thus their spontaneous comments, recorded in the early reports of local School Medical Officers, help to fill a gap on a previous generation which was not subject to such regular and close scrutiny. First and foremost, it is clear that families resented interference with conditions which they took for granted. Many, whose children were otherwise clean, thought little of verminous hair, and were outraged when it was pointed out to them. Head sores they dismissed as 'heat sores'. They insisted that 'some heads breed lice' and that 'it was in the blood'.[10] The belief that vermin was a sign of health was firmly held and was to persist into the inter-war period in the twentieth century. How else, parents argued, could a child support the life of the parasite as well as his own life? They were to resist compulsory cleansing even in cases where the head was a crawling, matted mass of vermin and dirt, the removal of which left the scalp covered with naked sores. A strange distinction was made by some mothers between girls and boys; they regularly washed their daughters' clothing but never that of their sons, from the day it was new until it was discarded.[11]

Simultaneously the new system of local health visitors brought to light survivals of traditional practices in infant upbringing. There was, for example, the custom of not allowing the child to see daylight until it was several months old, and of *never* bathing it. Newly appointed visitors commonly went into homes where mothers of three or four children admitted they had never given them as babies a proper bath and were horror-stricken at the suggestion.[12] They found babies kept in airless rooms or even worse conditions, as in the case of one Blackburn infant whose cradle was alongside the dog kennel in what the mother considered to be the most comfortable corner of the room, the recess underneath the stairs. The baby in the cradle was next to three dogs in the kennel.[13]

In the late nineteenth century, however, the medical examination of schoolchildren still lay in the future. Contemporary evidence came from the new sanitary and medical authorities in the municipalities. Theirs was a crusade against dirt and it was one which was pursued with ever greater vigour against sections of the urban populations who, in the words of one medical officer, 'were utterly regardless of cleanly surroundings . . .', whose skin and clothes were filthy.[14] The stress of such evidence was on abuses to be eradicated, on attitudes of 'ignorance', 'superstition', 'stubbornness' and 'unreasoning custom' to be changed. Above all, the descriptions were of the lazy and uncaring.

It is usually only by inference that there are glimpses of families which even in the worst areas waged unceasing war against infesting dirt. Of Angel Meadow, a notorious part of Manchester, a survey in 1897 noted 'a sprinkling of old families, long-settled, hard-working, respectable, clean in person and home'.[15] There were similar 'bright spots' in Salford, described by the volunteers of the Ladies' Health Society: '. . . clean homes, pretty little sitting-room kitchens, pictures on the wall, clean hearths, chests of highly-polished mahogany drawers, a steady husband, a tidy wife and children'.[16]

Overall, in the communities there were many who by endless scrubbing, mopping and scouring of sanded stone floors kept homes clean. Carbolic soap was in regular use for washing, and tin baths were brought out as a Friday night ritual. Children's hair was carefully attended to either by a weekly wash in strong soda water or by firm rubbing with 'chemist's precipitate', described by one contemporary as 'strong enough to kill tigers'.[17] Washing day itself was a major operation and through the week damp washing was everywhere. It was, of course, much easier in the respectable 'two up and two down' or even better houses; the odds were heavily weighted against those who lived in 'blocks of hovels sharing a single tap, earth closet and open midden; each house with a candle for light, an oil lamp or a bare gas jet'.[18] Here the struggle for cleanliness was often more than could be managed.

The observer in the streets could see at a glance the contrasts in physical appearance of children. Hair, skin, stature, as well as clothing and footwear, were indicators of the homes. The passer-by, however, saw only the outer clothing, usually dark and durable (with lighter, washable pinafores for the girls) in respectable families and ill-fitting, often second-hand, garments in the less respectable. Underneath the contrast was even more marked; on the one hand, layers of woollens against the cold and the damp, including for the girls, red flannel petticoats (with something better for Sundays);[19] on the other, at worst, clothing stitched together for the winter and padded with newspaper.[20]

Everywhere the death rate reflected location and parental occupation. In Macclesfield, for example, there was a remarkable contrast between the statistics of the well paved and sewered districts of the north and west and those of the congested and insanitary streets in the east. While the infant mortality in 1890 was estimated at 80 per 1,000 births for the upper and professional classes, chiefly resident in the healthier areas, the general town average was 200.[21] In Blackburn the following year the infantile death rate for the offspring of cotton workers and labourers was 254 per 1,000 births, compared with 160 for the offspring of all other parents.[22] Such a death toll cut down the natural increase of population.

As in the past, the high infantile mortality was commonly attributed to the employment of mothers in factories. The medical officer of Macclesfield, however, pointed out that many families would be worse off if mothers did not go out to work and that, if couples could not afford marriage, there would be an increase in illegitimacy. As he later illustrated, it was not the factory districts within the town that had the highest infantile death rate. Quite the contrary; in two districts, Hurdsfield and East Macclesfield, both similar in sanitary provision, the former, which provided full work in its cotton and silk mills, recorded only half the proportion of infant deaths of its non-industrial neighbour.[23] Poverty, in his opinion, was the main cause of loss of infant life. In Manchester, similarly, some of the worst statistics related to non-factory districts.

In fact infantile mortality rates were the result of a combination of circumstances. One factor certainly was the proportion of working wives of child-bearing age. Thus high rates were regularly recorded in the weaving districts of Blackburn, Preston and Burnley where women on four looms were nearly as well paid as male operatives.[24] Similarly, Stockport, despite its situation in a spinning area which offered lower wages to women, had a strong tradition of female factory employment and, apparently, an unusually high proportion of working mothers. Here, even in the closing years of the century, one out of every four infants died before the age of twelve months, about one in ten within the first week of life and one in five within the first month.[25]

However, it would be misleading to consider a single factor in isolation. Site, soil structure, degree of overcrowding and progress in sanitary reform were all relevant. Stockport, for example, lagged well behind most towns of similar size in the last respect; not only that, the river Tame, which flowed through its centre, was notorious for 'receiving the sewage of 100,000 dwellers on its banks before it reached the town'.[26] Even between neighbouring textile centres mortality patterns differed, depending on size and proximity to country air. Hence the smaller weaving towns of Colne and Nelson had significantly lower death rates than adjacent older towns like Burnley.[27]

Medical opinion favoured the establishment of nurseries for working mothers but in practice, where an individual employer or volunteers took the initiative, there was little response from women, who preferred to leave their children with people they knew. Nurseries at Ashton, Blackburn, Burnley and Preston were tried without success. Among the few to survive for any length of time were those in Ancoats and in Patricroft, Eccles. The latter, founded in 1877 with the encouragement of the medical officer, was certainly functioning well into the '90s. Open from 5.45 a.m. to 7.00 p.m., children—mostly infants—were cared for and, when possible, were wheeled out in turn in a large basket perambulator holding eight![28]

In general, however, the babies who were taken into the street in the early morning, wrapped in their mothers' shawls or even carried in cradles by their fathers, were on their way to child-minders. Some women took in a number of infants. One doctor described his experiences in Manchester, where he had seen as many as six children asleep in a large soap box.[29] There were notorious cases of neglect. In 1889, an inquest was held on the death of a twelve-week-old child of a carding-room hand in Blackburn. According to the report,

The mother stated that she was in the habit of taking her child at 5.30 in the morning to be nursed by an old woman to whom she gave 5 shillings a week. Twice a week she came back to dinner but at other times she did not return until night. On the day in question she returned at noon and found the child dead on two chairs where she had placed it. The child was on its back with its face covered with bedclothes. The old woman stated she had not given the child anything to eat that morning, and that she got up at two o'clock because she had nothing else to do.[30]

Though the extensive kinship networks of the past may have shrunk, many mothers, whether they were working or not, relied on the help of their own mothers. Often childbirth brought mother and daughter closer together, perhaps closer than they had ever been before. The grandmother now acquired status and a sense of superiority. She was usually near by with a welcome pair of hands and, with the confidence of experience, had a ready solution for most ailments which harassed the mother herself. Dogmatic and forceful, often she had nothing but ridicule and scorn for 'new-fangled' ideas. It was her advice which was heeded more than that of the medical authorities, which appeared in the form of public placards and leaflets given out at the registration of births. Reformers often expressed their frustration. As one medical officer later wrote,

the great stumbling-block of our efforts is the ignorance and obstinacy of the grandmother who assures us that she reared her family on biscuits and tea and pobs from a month old, and when her children had measles she never called in a doctor but gave them saffron and whisky and other such remedies, and took care not to wash them until the attack was over.[31]

Other doctors condemned as superstitious the belief that the weighing of babies, which came in with the early health visitors at the turn of the century was unlucky. The instance was quoted of one grandmother who declared that she would have her daughter prosecuted for manslaughter should the child die after having been weighed.[32] With the wisdom of hindsight James Niven, a former medical officer with some forty years' experience in Lancashire towns, wrote, 'The habits of generations are not to be altered in a day, and perhaps one does not sufficiently appreciate how much young industrial mothers are dependent on their mothers and grandmothers, even if they wish themselves to follow the advice given them.'[33] Few had the courage to break with tradition and the expectations of friends and relatives.

As food became available more cheaply and in greater variety families fed better. Over half a century most of the basic foods had halved in price.[34] There was more citrus fruit; former factory girls have recalled taking home oranges bought at two for a farthing at the mill gates on Friday nights. The opening of branches of co-operative societies afforded a chance of better value for money. There were, however, frequent references to local traders selling adulterated goods: cheap butter made of grease from horses' bones and lard mixed with ground rice.[35] Milk, at threepence or fourpence a quart, was purchased sparingly. Bought from corner shops in the towns or from churns in the streets it was frequently heavily diluted, adulterated and so dirty that even the 'boldest itinerants poured the last grey inch away'.[36]

Always complaints were made against women—that they had no sense of managing households, that their food purchases were irrational and that their cheerless homes drove husbands to drink. Of girls about to be married one Manchester physician wrote, 'These children of labour are, for the most part, as ignorant as a savage in the art of preparing an acceptable meal, even of the simplest kind.'[37] Other commentaries, even of families in the same area, were more tempered. Mary Dendy, who as an active member of the City School Board saw a good deal of Manchester schoolchildren, noted that their families cooked on Saturdays. 'They have an enormous supper on Saturday night. On Sunday they have the meat cold. On Monday there will be something left. On Tuesday, Wednesday, Thursday and Friday children have their pennies to go to the shop and naturally they look underfed.'[38] There were, however, incidental references by contemporaries to the poorest households in neighbouring Salford, where economical stews and sheeps' heads were constantly simmering on the hob.[39]

Life was very different in smaller towns where thrift and frugality were second nature to many. Beatrice Webb, who on her visits to Bacup came to know mill families well, noted that women baked their own bread but that main meals were often oatmeal and cheese, a diet which she found strangely 'farinaceous'. She wrote, 'This class eats too little . . .' and she mentioned the practice of sending adolescents off to work on only a drink of tea.[40]

Something of the inside story is glimpsed from the recollections of

Hilda Snape of her childhood in a working-class family in Bolton at the turn of the twentieth century.[41] Her mother, left a widow with two young children, had supported them by washing and baking before her remarriage. Even afterwards, with a second family, it was a struggle to make ends meet, especially when, in his job as a carter, injury befell the father. The daughter recalls—almost incidentally and with no sense of self-pity—her household tasks before she went, at the age of twelve, to the factory as a half-timer. Just a few of the chores were to collect and return washing, which was still taken in, help with the heavy work of mangling as well as the careful laundering of the numerous pairs of lace curtains, scrub and scour the stone-flagged kitchen floor and run errands, including, prior to the weekly baking day, going with a specially provided pillow case for 'a dozen of flour and a quarter of barm'. It was a training familiar to many, and one which even severe critics of the Lancashire housewife would not have thought amiss.

Many of the skilled textile operatives were among the best-paid labour in the country, but those who were unskilled and semi-skilled both in the textile and supporting trades earned barely enough to cover the needs of large families. Of the food available it was the custom in many households for wage-earners to eat first and children last. Hilda Snape recalled, 'small children never had a whole egg except on Easter morning for breakfast. Other times we made do with the tops from the grown ups'.[42] In Salford Robert Roberts noted that girls fared particularly badly: 'mothers felt that they didn't need much—"not the same as lads". In the streets, therefore, none looked more pathetically "clemmed" than the little schoolgirl.'[43] In the numerous households brought low by drunkenness, children, and often mothers, were defenceless victims. Among the latter there were many who by work in the mill or at the mangle saved families from crushing poverty which drunken fathers would have inflicted. Such women frequently bore enfeebled offspring; in the words of one child specialist, they were 'poor mothers who have lived the lives of hard wear and tear during pregnancy, are themselves badly nourished and weakly and have felt the pinch of poverty . . .'.[44]

In the weaving towns, where more women than men were employed in the factories, the latter had frequently to take on lower-paid labouring jobs. From Preston a woman factory inspector reported at the turn of the century that men looked for wives who were good four-loom weavers and that the former had a reputation for being lazy. She referred to women weavers who had lost many of their children as infants; one had buried nine of her thirteen children.[45]

On the other hand, the skill of the women operatives was frequently an insurance against family disaster. Left as widows with young children—not an infrequent occurrence—they were able to provide for them out of wages which were often well over twenty shillings a week. As an investigation undertaken in Rochdale in 1907 revealed, it was not women such as this who sought public relief but others who could do little but take in washing.[46]

On the evidence of Robert Roberts of Salford, only the shrewdness and self-sacrifice of his mother, formerly a factory worker from the age of nine, saved her children from calamities which an unreliable father would have brought on them. There were many such women who bore the brunt of rearing and maintaining their children. In order to provide as well as they did for their unborn children, many were said to 'tax themselves beyond measure . . . in tacit obedience to the great law of maternity'.[47]

III CHILD MORTALITY AND DISEASE

Throughout the latter years of the nineteenth century the infantile mortality rate in the region remained depressingly high. In the '70s and '80s there were large towns elsewhere, particularly Leicester, Liverpool, Nottingham and Norwich, with higher infant mortality. By the '90s, however, the pattern had changed, and with monotonous regularity it was textile towns that were recording the worst figures. In 1895, compared with the national average infantile mortality rate of 161 for every 1,000 births and 182 in the thirty-three great towns, the three towns in the latter category registering the highest rates were Preston (248), Blackburn (236) and Stockport (231). For the decade 1887–96 the highest rates were in Preston, Burnley and Blackburn, and of the ten towns listed as having the heaviest infantile mortality, seven were cotton towns. Among them only Leicester, Liverpool and Wolverhampton were outside the textile area.[1]

In addition to recorded deaths there were unknown numbers of still-births for which there were no registrations. It was well known that miscarriages were procured by a variety of means. Pills made of lead plaster were taken, as well as doses of quinine or slippery elm mixture, while the knitting needle was also commonly used.[2] Robert Roberts indicated usual methods in Salford including 'massive doses of penny royal syrup'. 'The "old queens" favoured concoctions of aloes and the vigorous use of turpentine. The "controlled fall" downstairs also had its advocates. But if all else failed someone always knew a women who knew a woman who . . .'.[3] Even at the end of the century a midwife's note was all that was required for burial purposes. There were midwives who were known to have certified for burial infants who had been born alive.[4]

There were also deaths which the authorities shrank from investigating. There was thus little to prevent infants, who had lived briefly being conveyed to a nameless grave. That such was the fate of many unwanted illegitimate offspring had long been suspected. Even so, the known death rate of illegitimate children was enormous; often as many as 70 per cent perished within the first year.[5] In Manchester, where unmarried women, excluded from the services of the trained midwives of the Lying-in Hospital, were said to employ 'the lowest and most incompetent class of midwives', it was hardly surprising that many infants scarcely breathed before they were cut off or that some suffered seriously from such after-effects as purulent discharge. In other towns there were no lying-in hospitals and most women, married or not, had little choice of midwife. They relied on the 'handy woman' who served in most emergencies, including laying out the dead. If she was not too particular in her habits she carried infection with her. Even after trained midwives were available the 'handy woman' was often preferred because she made herself generally useful in the house and looked after the children. There were doubtless instances of midwives who found favour because, as was reported from across the Pennines, they were known to have 'a lot of churchyard luck'.[6]

Many of the infants were listed as dying of atrophy, convulsions and syphilis, though in the last case the cause of death was often camouflaged, since otherwise the family would be debarred from drawing insurance benefit.[7] In many cases the records were misleading and concealed, perhaps, injury at birth and the effects of unsuitable feeding. There were also infants suffocated by overlaying, the result often of weekend drunkenness. Some deaths were attributed to the mothers' premature return to work. In Bolton, for example, it was calculated that the average absence for childbirth was two weeks.[8] However, as has been indicated, mill work by mothers was only one of several factors contributing to the high infant mortality rate, and other regions had dismal records, such as the colliery districts of the North-east and South Wales where there was no tradition of mothers working.

It was in the crowded centres, particularly during the hot summers, that diarrhoea struck the infant population. By means of placards, handbills and by printed instructions given on registration of births families were urged to take precautions by providing suitable food and attending to cleanliness. They were exhorted not to store food in dank, airless cellars. Where breast-feeding was not possible, mothers were advised on an alternative, usually milk and sugar added to the water in which pearl barley had been boiled. They were urged not to give infants 'just what you have yourselves', and under no circumstances to give 'beer, wine, spirits, tea, coffee, currants, new bread or unripe fruit'.[9]

Doctors complained that they could not convince parents that infants did not require solid or semi-solid food; the weaker and thinner the babies became, the more they were plied with starchy food and port wine.[10] There were descriptions of bread-and-milk which was left on the hob and went sour. The dangers of misfeeding were compounded by the over-use of purgatives and the administration of teething and cooling powders.

General lack of hygiene was another hazard. When babies cried, their gums were rubbed with dirty fingers, they were given dirty 'comforters' to suck and put down on dirty floors. At the turn of the century Dr Ashby, physician at the Manchester Children's Hospital, noted the general use of 'india rubber nipples' to which he attributed sore throats, enlarged glands and diarrhoea. 'In our Outpatient Department I see the "teat" drop on the floor where the dust is full of tuberculous germs and all sorts of things, and then the mothers put it straight into the mouths again.'[11]

The infantile death rate was highest in hot, dry summers. Indeed, the hot summers could be picked out as easily from mortality records as from those of the Meteorological Office. Heavy rainfall and colder weather lowered the death rate immediately. Breast-fed babies were rarely affected. One of the physicians of the Manchester Clinical Hospital who examined many Jewish babies noted that, because it was the custom of Jewish mothers to suckle their young, few suffered from diarrhoea or rickets even though they came from the poorest and dirtiest areas. He wrote, '. . . although the diarrhoea microbe may be swarming, it has no opportunity of contaminating the nourishment which the child receives'. Of other infants he described his revulsion at the smell of their feeding bottles, which had 'little flakes of curdled milk clinging to the sides and the tube caked with putrescent masses'.[12]

It was estimated that in Manchester infants fed by hand or by bottle during the first three months of life were fifty times as likely to die of diarrhoea as breast-fed children.[13] Over the area as a whole the death rate in the first three months of infancy was 50 per cent higher than in the main rural regions. However, according to the Registrar General in 1889, the destructive influences were much more intense during the succeeding period of infancy, that is, from three to twelve months, when the mortality rate was double that of the southern agricultural counties.[14]

By the later years of the century a variety of tinned foods for infants were available from chemists, including Savory & Moore's, Nestle's, Ridge's and Hards'. Such foods were recommended by dispensaries for mixed feeding between the ages of seven and twelve months. Poor families, however, purchased the cheapest tinned milk, which sold at $3\frac{1}{2}d$ for two tins and contained mostly sugar. There were many infants who received little else and who were subjected to a process of slow starvation.[15]

Access to fresh milk and the general environment of individual towns affected infantile death rate. Stockport, Salford and Manchester had the highest death rates from diarrhoea, often twice that of London or, indeed, the average for large towns. In the mid-'90s 40 per cent of infant deaths in Manchester were attributable to the one cause. In two months alone in 1894 there were 500 deaths.[16] Everywhere the death rate was highest in those parts of the towns which were notoriously ill drained and badly sewered.

In many areas the corporations provided 'diarrhoea mixture' which could be collected free of charge from police stations. In an effort to encourage cleanliness and hygiene they lent whitewash brushes and gave lime and disinfectant. Some households engaged in a constant battle against the hoards of horse-flies and bluebottles which invaded their kitchens and against bed bugs upstairs.

They lime-washed the bedrooms ('bug binding' was the delicate term for this) and drenched them with 'Klenzit Kleener' disinfectant. The blue flames of blowlamps licked spring mattress, floorboard, cracked walls and ceilings, but still they came, creeping along joists and through party walls until even the valiant cleanly housewife gave up in despair and prayed for cold weather.[17]

Above the age of infancy children took their chance with the usual infections. Epidemics of measles were frequent and broke out as soon as those who were unprotected formed what was called 'an explosive ratio'. Few escaped the virulent epidemics of the closing years of the century. Over the nation as a whole in the decade of the '80s the death rate of children with measles was higher than the combined rate from smallpox, scarlet fever, diphtheria and typhoid fever.[18] In Blackburn alone in 1895 324 children died of measles, and in the same year almost 500 in Manchester.[19] Many deaths, however, were associated with poor living conditions, so that it was possible to 'chalk out the graduations of the districts as regards poverty by adding up the death rates from measles for a number of years'.[20] Precisely the same was true of whooping-cough, which was seldom fatal to children of the well-to-do and where death was often a result of exposure of children to all weathers. Both infections were popularly regarded as normal hazards of childhood. The so-called chink-cough was to be heard from infants carried outside, from children at play and those in classrooms.

It was not only the death rates which caused concern. There were many after-effects. Teachers noted that some children appeared dull and stupid after absence from measles, actually a consequence of deafness left by the disease. The more they tried to teach them, the hazier they became. A serious after-effect of measles and whooping cough for some children was weakening of the lungs which left them easy prey to pneumonia and tuberculosis. It was well known that the origin of many adult cases of consumption lay in earlier attacks of measles or whooping-cough.

Unlike measles and whooping-cough, scarlet fever, as a notifiable

NORMAL PERIODS OF LATENCY, PREMONITORY FEVER, DURATION OF FEVER AND LENGTH
OF INFECTIVENESS OF SOME OF

THE CONTAGIOUS DISORDERS

{ SMALL POX

MODIFIED D°.

{ CHICKEN POX

MEASLES

{ GERMAN D°.

{ SCARLATINA

DIPHTHERIA

IDIOPATHIC ERYSIPELAS

{ TYPHUS

TYPHOID

{ MUMPS

The point of departure is taken from the day of the first appearance of the rash (in Diphtheria and Mumps the false membrane or swelling of the Glands) as being the most definite and characteristic phenomenon, and from which point the calculation is made to the left in estimating the probable time of inception, or to the right for freedom from infection.

1 ▬▬▬ – *Period of absolute Latency.*	1 + 2 – *Period of incubation.*	
2 ▨▨▨ – *Period of Fever before the rash.*	2 + 3 – *Period of Fever.*	
3 ▩▩▩ – *Period of Fever subsequent to the first appearance of the rash.*	2 + 3 + 4 – *Period of possible infectiveness.*	
4 ⣿⣿⣿ – *Period of infectiveness subsequent to the Fever.*		

disease, could be tackled by the local health authorities. Every four or five years it assumed epidemic proportions and by the '70s was described by one Medical Officer of Health as 'the scourge *par excellence* of our large manufacturing towns'.[21] Wigan, with a population of 50,000, recorded in 1884 a death toll of 200 from scarlet fever in just nine months.[22] Infection was airborne. There were instances of it being spread by milk sellers from street to street. Commonly it came also from second-hand or pawned clothing. Indeed, sometimes the source of an outbreak could be traced to a pawnshop or at other times to an individual dressmaker, as in Salford in 1879 when clothing for the Whitsun holiday was made in a shop where there was a malignant case of scarlet fever.[23]

Infected children could be excluded from schools, but there was nothing to stop half-timers going to work or, indeed, to prevent children wandering outside while at the peeling and infectious stage. Gradually, as opposition to isolation hospitals was overcome, by the later years of the century an increasing proportion of scarlet fever cases were removed for isolation. In many areas, however, there were no such facilities. At best, families disinfected their homes but many took no precautions against the spread of the disease. It was not unusual for healthy offspring to occupy the same bed as infected siblings. Because of the custom of visiting the dead and holding large funerals, neighbouring children as well as relatives caught the infection. There were occasions when magistrates ordered the removal to the mortuary of bodies of children who had died from scarlet fever on account of the number of visitors crowding into homes.[24] After-effects among those who had apparently recovered were frequently the unhappy consequence of exposure and left children prone to a variety of complaints: inflammation of the kidneys, dropsy, heart disease, swollen neck glands and discharge of the ears.

Though smallpox had ceased to be the main killer disease of the young, sporadic outbreaks, as in the epidemic years of the '70s, still roused fear and panic. In 1876 the alarm was so great in the Pendleton area of Salford that one street was barricaded and a black flag hoisted to warn off all who approached.[25] It was during this epidemic that the medical officer responsible for the Swinton Industrial School earned the public approbation of the Manchester Guardians by his prompt re-vaccination of almost 600 children, which arrested the spread of the infection.[26] However, in general, because scarlet fever and measles had removed large numbers of young children who would otherwise have been struck down, child deaths over the region were a small proportion of the whole and were confined to the unvaccinated or those insufficiently vaccinated with no trace of scab. Similar localised outbreaks in following years also affected unvaccinated children.

As well as smallpox there were typhoid fever epidemics which caused child deaths. Typhoid had long been recognised as a filth disease, and usually victims came from notorious slums. In 1880, of the twenty-eight typhoid patients in the Children's Hospital, five came from a single court in Deansgate.[27] Very often it was children who were in the habit of playing over street grids, near middens and among stagnant water who were struck down.

Most fatal of all infections was diphtheria. It was often difficult to diagnose from other causes of inflammation of the throat, and separate provision in many of the isolation hospitals was a late development. As with typhoid, diphtheria was commonly, though mistakenly, associated with environmental conditions, polluted soil, poor drainage and sewerage. It was endemic in urban areas, particularly in dry seasons, and highly contagious. Schools themselves were sources of infection which was passed on through slates and pencils, by class intonation where children breathed into each other's faces, by the use of a communal iron cup attached to an outside tap and by the habitual sharing of toffee sticks and tin whistles which were passed from mouth to mouth.

Medical authorities were horrified to discover that, in certain Church schools, after outbreaks of diphtheria children were lined up before the coffin to inspect their dead companion before the funeral procession moved off.[28] They were apparently powerless to carry out the recommended practice, namely, that the funeral should be private and that the body should be wrapped in a sheet soaked in a corrosive-sublimate solution and placed in a closely sealed coffin. Despite antitoxin serum, which became available from the '90s and increased facilities for isolation, the death rate remained high. While by the end of the nineteenth century substantial progress had been made in bringing other infections under control, diphtheria continued to be a serious menace.

Among constitutional diseases, as distinct from infections, tuberculosis remained, for young children as for adults, one of the main causes of death. It was accepted as an act of God, a mysterious malady for which there was no cure. Infants above the age of six months were also affected, and in 1879 the Manchester Clinical Hospital recorded the increase in infantile consumption as the most remarkable feature of admissions.[29] Tuberculosis, in its pulmonary form (phthisis), was associated with poor environmental conditions, including dampness and pollution, as well as with underfeeding and hereditary predisposition. Often it happened that an earlier infectious disease had left the lungs in a weakened condition. In its intestinal form it was frequently caused by infected milk. Even the Manchester Children's Hospital found it impossible to obtain milk which was guaranteed free from tuberculosis and from the '90s was using sterilised milk.[30]

Both forms of tuberculosis were preventable but only by the application of energetic measures over a considerable period. Malnutrition and overcrowding, probably the most serious causes, were hardest to combat and were not effectively tackled till the twentieth century. In many cases it was a 'house disease', and there were tragic circumstances in which whole families sank. Frequently it was the father of a family who first suffered. The mother herself would seek work, then the children, ill nourished and left at home with their father, caught the disease and the 'plague' was perpetuated.

Nationally, tuberculosis was responsible for about six per cent of deaths of infants. In Salford the rate was half as high again and included considerable numbers of deaths from tuberculous meningitis (inflammation of the brain).[31] Even so, mortality statistics probably understated the problem, since often death was not attributed to the underlying primary disease. Moreover death was far from being the whole story, for survivors including children with tuberculosis of the joints and spine, swelled the numbers of permanent cripples. A few were sent to homes for incurables, but most were left in the hostile urban environment.

Rickets, long considered a disease of the industrial poor, was often a cause—by reason of injury to the chest and tissues—of pulmonary tuberculosis. It had other long-term effects which undermined health, sometimes to such an extent that children succumbed to epilepsy and even insanity. In fact the worse cases of rickets were associated with mental 'enfeeblement; among those severely affected also were some who were classified as '*bona fide* dwarfs'.[32] Usually rickety deformities were amenable to treatment if advice was sought early enough. But many parents were so used to the condition that it was often difficult to persuade them to seek help.

While certain physical conditions of childhood were linked with factory work, there were nervous disorders such as chorea, which were accentuated by the pressures of school life. Though chorea had been known in the past, it was now more common. Referred to as 'brain fever', it was often associated with rheumatism and heart disease and was attributed to the 'forcing' system which teachers used to bring children up to the standards of the annual examinations. For children who were inadequately fed and weakly, overpressure could lead to collapse.

As a whole, the death rate of young children declined in the closing decades of the century, a consequence of a number of factors, including more rigorous measures for vaccination and the incidence of a milder type of scarlet fever. The infantile death rate, however, remained high, particularly in the industrial towns of the North-west. Some of the diseases were incurable; tuberculous meningitis, for example, once it had developed, was fatal to rich and poor alike. Most could have been prevented and their toll on life was a prodigal waste. The judgement of the famous physician of the Manchester Children's Hospital, Borchardt, in 1862, 'we have not yet practically comprehended the first great problem of social life—the preservation of the individual',[33] was scarcely less valid forty years on.

IV FAMILY SELF-HELP

Most children, as Robert Roberts described, accepted stoically the knocks, bruises and ailments that came their way.[1] The healthier the parents the more likely they were to have healthy children. Robust themselves, many adults held a philosophy similar to that attributed to Henry Browne, one of the staff of the Manchester Royal Infirmary: 'Keep your bowels open, trust in the Lord and wear flannel next to the skin.'[2]

Thus parents ignored apparently trivial complaints. When children demurred at venturing out in wind and rain they were brusquely reminded that since they were neither butter nor sugar they wouldn't melt, and were sent on their way. Inexplicable aches were dismissed as 'growing pains'. Old people today recollect the common maladies of their childhood, ear ache, chilblains and the like, and the home-spun remedies that were applied. Especially they remember the grease which was rubbed in to relieve chest complaints, the collop of bacon stitched on to flannel and worn on the neck for sore throat and the stewed comfrey used to bathe injured limbs and sprains. In the smaller towns particularly, where there were still thriving botanical societies, parents themselves might have a practical knowledge of herbal remedies or could call on a relative or neighbour. In such households there was no hesitation what to do; at the first sign of scarlet fever, for example, the child would straightaway be given home-brewed yarrow tea to bring out the sweat.[3]

Other parents possibly sought advice at a herbalist's shop or market stall or purchased a quack remedy. Perhaps because of the former link between local chapels and herbalism, medical authorities, even in the early twentieth century, still connected Nonconformity with quack medicine.[4] For most people, however, the expense of calling in the doctor was frightening. His charges with medicine—of the order of at least 2s 6d a visit—mounted up quickly and had usually to be paid off by instalments. Under some local schemes surgeries were held by a 'sixpenny doctor', but he was usually an unqualified assistant to a practitioner.[5]

There were new dispensaries, such as that at Eccles opened in 1877. As the authorities pointed out, only those who had experienced it could imagine the cruel penance of the long journey into Manchester and waiting for hours in crowded rooms.[6] More particularly was this true of those taking sick children. However, many families still had effectively no access to a dispensary and many others, quite apart from the difficulty of obtaining a recommendation, were excluded by the income limits set by the institution for 'proper objects of charity'. For instance, according to the rules of the Chorlton upon Medlock Dispensary in 1870, no married couple with an income of 16s or more a week could seek treatment. The limit was extended by 2s a week for every child in the family. By the time the rules were revised in 1899, 21s was the upper limit for a married couple, with the additional allowance for each child still fixed at 2s.[7] It was, therefore, not the poorest who were cut off from charitable aid, it was those families who could barely afford to call in a doctor and who were tempted to resort instead to a cheaper alternative.

Among the pains which were dismissed as trivial was toothache. Dental decay was treated with general disdain. Bred to frugality, even artisan families who called in a doctor if they thought the occasion demanded it would not have dreamed of spending hard-earned money on dental treatment. The first visit many made to a dentist was to have all teeth extracted and replaced by false ones.

Common defects, which the school medical service was later to categorise, were taken for granted. Adenoids were barely noticed, yet adenoid growth frequently made children so deaf and listless in class that they were considered stupid. Skin diseases and minor disabilities of sight and hearing were largely ignored. As school doctors and nurses were later to discover, there were some strange misconceptions. There were parents who regarded head vermin as a symbol of health; there were others who positively welcomed signs of discharging ears in the belief that 'if it should stop the child would have fits'.[8] There was also a mythology of popular remedies, including, for ringworm of the scalp, treatment with ink and tobacco juice.

Not unnaturally, parents who had never been parted from their children were opposed to their entering hospital. It took some time to allay their fears; isolation hospitals particularly, since they were associated in folk memory with the old fever hospitals, were regarded with suspicion. Even voluntary infirmaries represented an alien institutional world, with their emphasis on hygiene and fresh air, clinical precision and discipline. Despite strict regulations parents smuggled in all kinds of unsuitable food. Just how apprehensive and distrustful they were, even of minor medical treatment, was to be revealed in their reactions to school clinics in the early years of the twentieth century. Some, alarmed at the possible effect of the treatment for a known disability, wrote abusive letters; others, in their resentment at their children being singled out for complaints they themselves had disregarded, threatened and in some cases actually committed acts of physical violence.[9] As for the children, it was a long time before they were to lose their fears of doctors and clinics and accept medical examinations as part of school routine.

With increasing literacy many mothers were lured by the glowing advertisements for patent and other medicines which appeared in ever-growing profusion in the local papers. Specious promises were made by the vendors of teething and fever powders who claimed to cure all the complaints of infancy and childhood. Local chemists offered their own products, such as gripe-water often specifically described as being 'without opium or laundanum' (and probably, in fact, merely sweetened bicarbonate of soda). Sold at $7\frac{1}{2}d$ or a shilling a bottle it was alleged to relieve 'Acidity, Wind, Convulsions, Flatulence, Whooping Cough, Measles, Fits and other distressing complaints . . .'.[10] Large chemists like Kay's at Stockport manufactured their own products for sale, both wholesale and retail. These included chilblain ointment, Cholera Bottle and, most famous of all, their cough mixture, 'Compound Essence of Linseed', commonly known as 'Kay's Compound'.

As well as local preparations there was a battery of advertisements by national firms in the popular press and also in the religious weeklies. Many made reference to children. There were, for example,

'Dr. Williams' Pink Pills for Pale People' which were said to relieve those suffering from consumption, St Vitus' Dance and rickets. Even the famous Holloway's pills were declared to be as efficacious for children as adults. They offered a cure for 'inflammation, abscesses, ulcerations, . . . billiousness, sick headaches, nervousness, sleeplessness . . .' as well as 'skin diseases of the most revolting character'. As 'Mother's Friend' they were described as 'invaluable in all Children's Complaints'. In fact their contents, analysed after Holloway's death in 1883 as aloes, powdered ginger and soap, were at best harmless.

It was in vain that corporations put up warning notices against patent medicines and quack remedies. Many infants were 'animated chemists' shops'. Indeed, the nearest chemist was often consulted as the next best thing to calling a doctor. To his shop infants were taken with teething problems, children with croup, inflammation of the lungs and a host of ailments; for the common infections of scarlet fever and whooping-cough his syrup of squills, a preparation from squill bulbs and often digitalis, was frequently sought. Children themselves were sent for poisonous substances, including white precipitate—mercuric oxide—for destroying head vermin, and scrupulous chemists confessed to living in fear of an inquest. The number of chemists' shops increased rapidly; in Manchester, for example, there was a more than fourfold increase over the half-century 1830–80, compared with a mere doubling of the number of doctors.[11]

Mixtures for common ailments were easily obtainable at small general shops. Flowers of sulphur was bought for sore throats; in a childhood recollection of early twentieth century Failsworth, 'our Mother used to buy it and blow it down our throats just as an ostler would blow powder and pills down the throats of his horses'.[12] Purgatives such as Gregory Powder, liquorice powder and California Syrup of Figs sold well, especially at the weekend, so also did 'Mother's Friend' (known colloquially in Salford as 'Knock-out Drops'). Laced with tincture of opium, it could be relied on to keep the infant in a coma till well into Sunday morning![13]

Those who, in contemporary terms, belonged to the respectable working class saw to it that they were provided for in time of sickness. Many as working children joined Sunday school sick societies and continued membership into adulthood. By the mid-'70s the famous Bennett Street Sunday School in Manchester had some 1,200 children enrolled in its sick club. Established members could claim relief of up to 5*s* 6*d* a week on production of a medical certificate. Customary causes of absence, named on certificates, were colic, colds and bronchitis, but some certificates which have survived were from hospitals and indicated treatment for specific complaints, including ophthalmia.[14]

Highly organised, with a rota of visitors and a system of fines in lieu of serving as visitors, such Sunday school societies were common throughout the textile area. They were particularly strong in the east Lancashire towns, where individual clubs in Accrington and Over Darwen had 800 to 900 members.[15] Often, of course, it was children brought up in the strong evangelical tradition in the towns and villages who were best equipped to resist disease. By family care and industry they were kept clean and well fed. Their upbringing reflected all aspects of home life, physical, social and moral.

Apart from religious organisations, there were from the early '70s for those who were able to pay regular weekly contributions—usually a penny for adults and a half-penny for children—a number of Provident Dispensaries. By 1876 there were seven such dispensaries in various parts of Manchester and Salford with 18,000 on their books.[16] To some extent they siphoned off from the charitable institutions those who could afford to pay, though in fact the drop in patients at the Children's Hospital and similar organisations was only temporary. Indeed, the numbers on the books of Provident Dispensaries grew only slightly and there were many complaints of the abuse of voluntary charities.

Little help was available to women in childbirth. Outside the larger centres there were, apart from minor charities, no agencies to assist mothers before, during and subsequent to giving birth. Most societies specifically excluded from benefit sickness in pregnancy or after childbirth. Exceptionally, as with the Stand Unitarian Sunday School Society, there was a grant for confinement. Here, according to the rules of 1869, 7*s* was paid to a member 'if the child be born in wedlock'. The Stand accounts of the '70s show payments of between three and fourteen grants annually, each equivalent to one and a half weeks' ordinary female sickness benefit.[17]

Such provision was unusual and would appear to have covered factory workers. Just how much of a struggle it was for a labourer's wife to lay a little aside in preparation for childbirth was described by an Oldham woman, a former domestic servant, who recalled her experience of the mid-'80s. From the early months of marriage she had regularly taken in sewing and washing to supplement the 15s 5d a week her husband gave her. As her pregnancy advanced she took in more work, 'anything to save a shilling or two', and in the last week earned just over 10s by making eight waistcoats. In consequence she suffered agonisingly from gathered breasts for three months.[18]

At birth families had to rely on their own resources. By contrast, they were helped to make provision for death, that is, for a respectable funeral. Hence babies were insured as soon as they were born, though in many cases the amount payable barely covered funeral expenses. Amounts of 25s for an infant under three months and two or three times as much for children over the age of six are mentioned as payments of urban clubs, but such sums were usually in excess of Sunday school societies' allowances. From such benefits families would have little to spare for the mourning clothes on which so much store was set, or on the customary funeral refreshments. The all-important thing, however, was 'to keep straight with the burial books ... to have a body put away on the parish was to bear a lifetime's stigma'.[19]

Death was accepted with fatalism. 'It's better off, and we have more left than we can keep,'[20] was a not uncommon remark. Because insurance was customarily paid on a sliding scale according to age, a typical statement overheard among mothers awaiting dispensary death certificates was 'Oh, I shall only get 30 shillings. But if the little fellow had lived another month he would have been entitled to £2'.[21]

From Manchester and Salford evidence continued to come of the so-called death clubs run from public houses where part of the benefit money was in drink. Physicians recorded cases of individual families; one had buried four out of five children (all four had died at ages between eleven and twenty-one months) and had received a total of £17 towards funerals, which were estimated to have cost barely a third of that amount, and, additionally, three shillings in drink at each death.[22] In fact legal restrictions on burial payments were largely evaded. Because certificates of death were needed to claim benefit, the dispensary doctor was called in, but only at the last moment. One reported that in fourteen cases children were in a state of coma on his first visit and died before he could see them again; there were another nine cases so hopeless that they died after a second visit.[23]

It was the disreputable town clubs that attracted publicity. By contrast there were, of course, many organisations in both urban and village communities officially registered under the Friendly Societies' Act and properly administered. In stable districts there were burial societies—sometimes even a single society—which covered the great majority of the population and in which infants were almost universally enrolled. Such was the case in the industrial village of Bollington, Cheshire, where the well-established burial society, known by the name of the inn where it met, the Holly Bush, had a membership by the early '70s of over 4,000, a high proportion of the entire community of cotton workers, miners, jobbing labourers and their families.[24] Infants could be entered from the age of four weeks if one or both parents were members. The generous payments irrespective of age, £1 2s 6d for those who had subscribed less than six months, and £5 to other members, reflected the general health of the community. They attracted not only parents in the village but out-members who had moved away to Oldham, Ashton or Denton and who together with the entrance fee sent the required doctor's certificate affirming their infant's good health and sound constitution. Among the common causes of death recorded on the certificates of young members were debility from birth, convulsions and bronchitis; occasionally death was attributed to burns and scalds, to 'tubercular meningitis' and even to 'hare lip operation three days from birth'.

Children everywhere were familiar with sickness and death. Usually the mother coped with the ailments as best she could, perhaps with help of relative or neighbour. For the common disorders, colds and coughs, boils and bruises she found remedies. The doctor, except in the more secure households or where his services were available under special schemes, was called only in emergencies. Fear of debt which could impoverish, even cripple, a family in critical years was a severe deterrent.

V PHILANTHROPIC ENDEAVOUR

By the 1870s many of the old dispensaries had expanded to include hospital provision. Whereas the original institutions had been in crowded urban centres, the hospitals were usually erected in spacious and healthier areas on the outskirts of towns. In location and design they reflected the influence of Florence Nightingale, as did their internal regime, based on trained nurses under the direction of matrons, skilled in 'the science of Nurse Superintendence'. High standards of hygiene and discipline were maintained. Everything possible was scrubbed and exposed to the fresh air; the emphasis of organisation was on briskness and efficiency.

The new Children's Hospital, opened in 1873 in a building four miles out of Manchester in Pendlebury and, as was proudly stated, '200 ft above Manchester town hall'[1] was a model of its kind. Each pavilion ward was well separated from the others so as to allow free circulation of air. Of the three original pavilions to be put into use, two were general wards and a third was exclusively for fever cases, serviced by special fever broughams; even the nurses of the fever ward had separate quarters so that the entire unit was wholly isolated. (The quiet of Pendlebury was in contrast to the bustling site of St Mary's in Quay Street which received children as well as childbirth cases. Here wooden pavements had to be laid so that patients could get to sleep.)[2]

Such was the appeal to girls of good families of work in the Manchester Children's Hospital that lady probationers were prepared to pay a premium for the privilege of training and submitted cheerfully to the stern discipline and to a regime which included duty rotas of sixty-three hours a week and attendance at prayers twice daily. So successful was the system—the lady probationers were much praised for the gentleness and refinement they brought to their work—that by 1881 the hospital was entirely staffed by 'gentlewomen'.

At first young children were officially excluded from the new infirmaries in the local towns. Gradually, however, they came to be admitted to general wards and by the latter years of the century most institutions had amended their rules and had special children's wards. In the Oldham Infirmary the Nichols ward for children was opened in 1878 and the rules were revised to admit children over four years old.

From its opening in 1883 the new building of the Bolton Infirmary had a separate children's wing, provided by a legacy under the will of a well known local benefactor. Blackburn and Preston Infirmaries had children's wards from the mid-'80s. Other later foundations, like the Victoria Hospital in Burnley, accommodated children in the women's wards in their early years.

Hospital for Sick Children, Pendlebury, Manchester, opened 1873. The plan shows the six pavilion wards. Each child had 98 square feet of floor space and 1,650 cubic feet of air space. The central blocks from front to rear housed the administrative offices and kitchens, the operation room and dispensary and the nurses' bedrooms

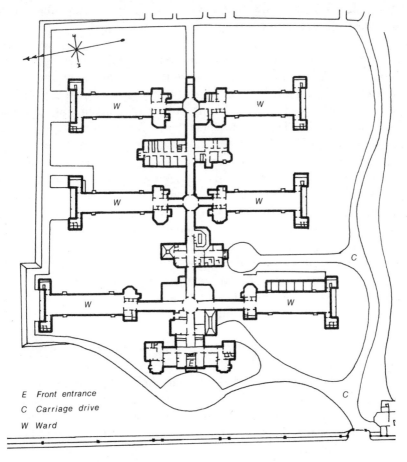

E   Front entrance
C   Carriage drive
W   Ward

In contrast to the new institutions, the major old-established infirmary of the region, the Manchester Royal, remained on its restricted central site. It had no separate children's wards, nor, unlike similar hospitals elsewhere, had it a separate ward for burns. Many young children, of course, came in with burns, as did older ones who were involved in industrial accidents. The smell associated with such cases was said to permeate the surgical wards. So limited was space that, since the ground floor was given up to out-patients, accidents, including burns, were received in the basement and removed thence to the upper floors by means of special beds on wheels. The latter were a particular feature of the Infirmary; constructed locally, they were covered with india rubber and provided with springs.[3]

It was not surprising that parents were fearful of their children's chances of survival in hospital. Before the general use of antiseptics lives were at risk both in medical and surgical wards. In the former, the customary ward sponge, wrung out only in warm water, spread infection; in the latter, erysipelas was commonly rife, almost epidemic. It was recalled of the Manchester Royal Infirmary in the early '70s that the theatre surgeons wore 'dirty mackintoshes or overcoats too old for ordinary use. They were never washed and the wearer seemed proud of the old blood in them.'[4] Here the records reveal child deaths after surgery. There was, for example the case of a two-year-old in 1872 who contracted erysipelas after the third operation for relief of deformity.[5]

For some time the use of antiseptics was a matter for individual surgeons. Already by 1872 one of the surgeons at the Manchester Royal Infirmary was using carbolic acid, while another preferred tincture of benzoin.[6] By the mid-'70s, however, it was reported that all cases were being treated according to Lister's antiseptic surgery. Even so, one of the pioneer users of antiseptics continued to operate in a blood-stained cassock.[7]

Almost simultaneously the use of anaesthetics transformed surgery. Even major operations could now be accomplished in a few minutes. In the past much had depended on the stamina of the individual patient, and with children there were occasions when a good deal of persuasion was required before surgery could be completed.[8] With anaesthetics operations for malformations and congenital distortions

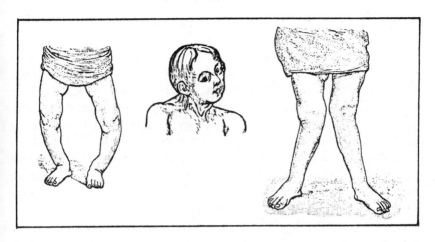

Examples of child deformities: (centre) wry neck, a form of muscular paralysis—this is a less severe case than that described on p. 76; (left) bow legs, and (right) knock knees, both associated with rickets

became more common.

In the medical wards of the new local hospitals children were admitted with nervous and heart diseases, rickets, and with various forms of tuberculosis. By the '90s in the Manchester Children's Hospital more than one-tenth of out-patients and two-fifths of in-patients were suffering from tuberculosis of the lungs, glands, brain or joints. One-third of deaths were from tuberculosis.[9] Rickets accounted for about a quarter of all patients at this and similar hospitals. Cod-liver oil had long been given to children suffering from rickets, and infirmaries and out-patient departments were now dispensing huge quantities. By the beginning of the twentieth century the Children's Hospital through the dispensary was providing seven tons, almost 2,500 gallons, of cod-liver oil emulsion annually.[10]

With the successful application of antisepsis certain of the rickety deformities became amenable to surgical treatment. From the late '70s there was a large increase in child surgical patients in both the local and regional hospitals. All were undertaking operations on rickety limbs, on tuberculous joints and bones and on children who were suffering from burns and fractures. Often, by the end of the century, almost a third of surgical operations in general hospitals were on children. However, despite extended provision in such hospitals many children from a wide area of Lancashire and Cheshire were referred to the special Manchester children's hospitals.

With the establishment of Provident Dispensaries in their immediate environment, these institutions now had a larger proportion of more serious ailments. In the words of the report of the Clinical Hospital in 1876, they were taking 'the principal share of the unmanageable and uncontrollable, like the sediment from a great mixture of impurities'. Already in 1879 one pavilion at the Children's Hospital had been set aside for surgical cases. In the early '90s there were about 500 operations each year and by the end of the century over 1,000. Some were for congenital malformations, including cleft palates and hare lips, but the majority were for diseases of the joints and bones and for the correction of rickety deformities, such as bow legs and knock knees. In 1895 a second ward was assigned to surgical cases. Even so, it could accommodate only a fraction of the children whom the dispensary doctors considered to be in need of treatment.

Exceptionally weakly patients 'went out' under anaesthetic. There was an inquest in January 1882 on a child who had died under chloroform at Pendlebury.[11] The patient had been suffering from abscess in the thigh as well as spinal disease and had died of shock during the rapid emptying of the abscess. Other deaths were reported, particularly from spinal surgery. In all hospitals operations on joints had frequently to be repeated. Children were then put into splints or given supports and built up with cod-liver oil.

By the '80s it had become customary to arrange a period of convalescence by the sea, and in 1895 the Children's Hospital erected its own convalescent home at St Annes on Sea, a spell in which did wonders for the recovery of the surgical patients. Unfortunately the benefits of operation and convalescence were often lost when the child returned to a slum environment. Many remained permanently in irons or confined to spinal chairs; others were dependent on surgical appliances. Such children were a common part of everyday life and some became helpless paupers.

As local infirmaries expanded they offered more extensive and varied treatment. Preston Infirmary, for example, opened an ophthalmic ward where many of the weavers, sometimes young teenagers, had to have an eye removed as a result of 'wounds from shuttles', an operation which the Manchester Eye Hospital had long been treating and which was similar to that for gunshot wounds in military surgery. Only in the '90s when shuttle guards were installed did the accidents cease.

Besides the new developments in medical and surgical treatment, the later years of the century brought increasing hospital provision for infectious diseases. Isolation had long been recognised as an effective method of containing outbreaks of fevers and smallpox, but once the epidemics had subsided temporary hospitals had been closed. The Manchester House of Recovery had been the exception, but even this had ceased as a separate institution at the mid-century when it had been amalgamated into the Infirmary, supposedly as an isolated ward on the top corridor. In fact, the only means of separation from the rest of the building was a wooden screen, the door of which was frequently left open.[12]

Dispensary doctors had long pressed for isolation facilities so that by prompt action outbreaks, particularly of scarlet fever and measles, could be confined. On its foundation the new Children's Hospital at Pendlebury had a pavilion set aside as a fever ward and similarly the Clinical Hospital had a separate wing built for the purpose in 1873. Both Manchester and Salford Corporations paid for beds for their own child patients, mostly suffering from scarlet fever. Salford Corporation, however, demurred at what it considered an excessive charge by the Children's Hospital of 2s a day for each patient. In the event each authority contracted to pay a block grant.

During epidemic years, as in 1875, the hospital had over 200 cases of scarlet fever, with deaths of the order of 15–18 per cent.[13] It had also numbers of diphtheria and typhoid patients. Strict rules were imposed on visitors, though there is no record that the medical staff's proposal that they should wash their hands in carbolic acid before leaving and while in the ward should wear special cloaks,[14] was implemented. Gradually the pattern of provision changed as the corporations made their own arrangements for isolation in specially designed hospitals. By 1897 the fever ward was no longer required at Pendlebury; it was adapted as a general ward and the special fever broughams were sold.

Throughout the latter years of the century the voluntary hospitals were extending their range of treatment. In 1872 St Mary's, Manchester, reported a delivery by Caesarean section, 'a rare and very critical case'.[15] By 1880 the Children's Hospital was applying the 'interrupted battery current' for cases of infantile paralysis.[16] Everywhere the scale and increasing diversity of treatment added to the expense. Some assistance came from annual Sunday and Saturday funds, collections in the churches and within the communities. In the local hospitals, as in certain dispensaries, charges were levied on families of patients over a modest income level. In general, support was precarious in such hospitals and individual patrons had to be solicited for assistance, even for particular items such as children's crutches and artificial limbs.

DIET TABLE.

MILK DIET.   MEAT DIET.

Breakfast—6-30 a.m.

Milk, ½ pt.   Milk or Cocoa, ½ pt.
Bread.   Bread, Butter or Dripping ;
Butter.   or
                               Porridge, and Bread and Butter.

Dinner—Noon.

Milk, ¼ pt.   Fresh Roast Mutton or Beef,
Milk Pudding.   minced—3 oz. when cooked.
                               Mashed Potatoes, 4 oz. ;
                                     or
                               Green Vegetables, with Rice or
                                   Bread.
                               Milk Pudding.
                                   Four days a week.
                               Soup, ½ pt., with Vegetables and
                                   Bread,
                               Milk Pudding.
                                   Three days a week.

Tea—4 p.m.

Milk, ¼ pt.   Milk or Cocoa, ½ pt.
Bread, 2 oz.   Bread.
Butter.   Butter or Dripping.

Supper—7 p.m.

Milk, ¼ pt.   Milk, ⅓ pt.
Bread, 2 oz.   Bread, Butter or Dripping.
Butter :   or
    or   Boiled Bread and Milk.
Boiled Bread and Milk.

For the specialist children's hospitals, the springs of charity flowed more freely. By 1878 almost £50,000 had been raised for the Children's Hospital at Pendlebury. In 1876 a grand bazaar in the Free Trade Hall in Manchester, a regional effort, since contributions came from the neighbouring towns, realised £21,000.[17] It was at this point that the institution was equipped for its full complement of 168 beds and thus became the second largest children's hospital in the country. In the mid-'90s there was apparently no difficulty in raising capital and maintenance costs for the convalescent home at St Annes. St Mary's and the Manchester Clinical Hospital drew on similar sources of benevolence, and all hospitals were at pains to record gifts in money and kind meticulously, including Christmas presents to children of bright new pennies, toys and clothing.

Hospitals relied on voluntary gifts of fruit to supplement hospital food. The accompanying diet sheet was included in the annual reports of the Children's Hospital for 1885 and for succeeding years into the '90s (see opposite).

The voluntary infirmaries made their greatest impact through their out-patients' departments. Every day waiting rooms were crowded. The proximity of bodies suffering from various diseases and infections was positively dangerous. To children particularly the atmosphere was awesome and often terrifying. One child, rushed to hospital with an arm so badly spiked that there seemed nothing for it but amputation, afterwards recalled, 'They put fourteen stitches in the arm while I sat dumb with fear, not through my injury, but petrified by the bevy of white vestments around.'[18]

In certain localities there were other sources of medical charity, including medical missions. Salford was exceptional in its mission dispensary, organised from 1875 by Dr Grimké in the former Ragged and Industrial School. Within an adjoining day nursery special provision was made for crippled children. Situated in Greengate, a district where even many years later it was said there was 'scarcely a straight-legged or healthy child to be seen', the scope for the charity was almost limitless. At a more modest level, as in Rochdale and Bolton, supporters of the parish church contributed towards the expense of a nurse to attend poor families and procure for weakly children gifts of clothing, food and cod-liver oil.[19] On similar lines but at a more ambitious level local initiative in the towns succeeded in setting up district Nursing Associations. Bolton, for example, had such an organisation from 1889 and built a nurses' home with accommodation for four nurses. Again the sick poor were given attention and helped by medical supplies and comforts. The associations also hired out nurses to private families.[20] Meanwhile in Manchester and Salford the highly organised system of home visitors under the aegis of the Ladies' Health Society had attracted support from the municipalities.

Altogether there was a great network of benevolent associations. Towns had their Cinderella Clubs, Country Holiday Funds and Fresh Air Funds, as well as charities which provided meals, clothing, boots and clogs. Here also were branches of the League of Pity, the Guild of Brave Poor Things and the Cripples' Help Association, as well as Children's Aid Societies which sponsored visits to seaside convalescent homes. Though children's causes never failed to attract philanthropic support, most of them had to struggle to make ends meet. There was, however, a general revulsion against any suggestion of a compulsory rate. In the words of a Manchester alderman, it would amount to 'Communism . . . The next thing would be asking for rate aid to feed and clothe people . . .'. The fear was that rate aid would dry up the springs of charity, 'would chill the sympathies . . . and destroy the personal element'.[21]

VI SOCIAL DISCIPLINES AND PUBLIC PROVISION

Nationally from the 1870s there was a more positive approach to health. In contrast to earlier permissive measures, legislation became compulsory. In particular the Public Health Act of 1872 designated sanitary areas each of which was required to appoint a Medical Officer of Health. The appointment of medical officers in the localities and the establishment of a sanitary code under which they were to operate heralded a new era.

Specific measures aided their efforts, including the requirement of notification of diseases (beginning with cholera in 1875 and later including other infectious diseases) and, from 1874, of a statement of the precise cause of death on death certificates. Meanwhile earlier legislation for compulsory vaccination was being enforced more stringently and with considerable success. From the '70s the effect of educational measures was to bring the mass of children under the control of the health authorities, and so enable prompt measures to be taken against the spread of infection. There was in 1891 even an attempt by law to prevent women returning to work within a month of childbirth.

The annual reports of the medical officers in the textile districts of the North-west record the extension of their activities in tackling problems of housing, sanitation, infection, pollution and food adulteration. Their belief was in the preventive approach, the rousing of a 'sanitary conscience' in order to remove the underlying causes of disease. They pressed for improvements in drainage, sewerage and sanitation, they closed the schools in order to curb epidemics, urged their authorities to establish hospitals for infectious patients and strove to alert ordinary householders to an awareness of health hazards.

Some municipalities were unresponsive and even reluctant to engage a full-time official. Blackburn, with a population of 80,000 in the mid-'70s employed only a part-time medical officer at £25 per annum.[1] Officers themselves had to overcome public complacency and inertia as well as popular resistance. They had, for example, to deal with the Irish, who clung to their old custom of keeping general livestock in their houses and were even known to have had their lobbies enclosed for hen roosts.

Generally the new authorities secured improvements—the closing of numbers of cellar dwellings, the paving of streets and in sanitation the change-over from the privy midden to the pail. Rochdale was one of the first towns to introduce the new system, which was adopted by Manchester in 1880. Everywhere there was further replacement of defective drains and sewers by glazed pipes and the transfer to municipalities of the ownership of water supplies. Controls were introduced on slaughterhouses, shippens and dairies; lodging houses were brought under inspection and regulation; more parks and public baths were opened.

However, many abuses remained. There was the black smoke which even on a bright sunny day cast such a haze that buildings a hundred yards away appeared blurred.[2] (It could even be a source of pride and satisfaction, since it signified trade, and hence was a measure of employment and prosperity.) There were the foul smells from debris and refuse in the rivers, which were so pestilential that, as in the Irwell at Salford, a child rescued from drowning died of the inhaled poison.[3] There was the persistence of the old privy system even in large towns like Stockport where the municipality organised night scavenging. There was also the sale of tainted food and adulterated milk from which the public were largely unprotected.

In order to cut down high infantile mortality rates medical officers sought to change traditional habits by means of publicity leaflets and handbills on feeding and cleanliness. They encouraged employers to set up nurseries, where working mothers could leave their offspring. In Manchester and Salford the municipalities subsidised from 1892 the voluntary system of home visitors which had been found to be the most effective method of influencing mothers; by the close of the century Stockport had appointed a health visitor whose duties included talks to schoolgirls based on the medical officer's booklet, *Suggestions as to the Feeding of Infants for use in Senior Classes of Girls' Schools*.[4]

In an effort to counter popular contempt for childhood infections, placards with titles such as 'Measles is a Fever' were mounted and handbills of 'Advice on the Prevention and Management of Infectious Diseases' displayed. Teachers were required to identify and report cases of infection and, particularly in cases of measles, measures were taken to close schools. Diphtheria was the most baffling, but so seriously was it regarded that on occasions when it threatened an area teachers were instructed to 'exclude all children suffering from sore throat—simple or otherwise'.[5] Public handbills explained the nature of the disease, while antitoxin was available for doctors from central police stations.

As the most effective means of curbing infections, particularly scarlet fever, medical officers continued to press for isolation hospitals. They quoted as a model the new Barnes House of Recovery, which, built in 1871 from private funds and sited in the country air of Monsall, had replaced the old fever wards of the Manchester Royal Infirmary. Often they were opposed by municipal authorities on grounds of expense, and it was not uncommon for the latter to procrastinate until an outbreak of smallpox forced them to take action.

Many officers themselves took the offensive. In Manchester with the death rate from scarlet fever running at over 500 a year in the early '70s, John Leigh did not mince words. Of such a death rate, he wrote, 'It is not a necessity; it is the result of apathy, indifference and neglect, on the part of the wealthy to provide the moderate means necessary to keep the destroyer from their own doors.'[6] In Macclesfield the medical officer countered opposition to expenditure on an isolation hospital by reference to loss of life in economic terms. In a detailed analysis he computed the monetary loss from scarlet fever in a single year at over £2,000. Out of 336 cases twenty-eight lives had been lost. He estimated that twenty-eight funerals at £5 each had cost £140, that medical attention at £1 10s each had been £504. The value of the lives cut short, based on Farr's calculation in the Registrar General's report (1873) at £56 for each life, amounted to £1,568; altogether a total of £2,212.[7]

Before they built their own isolation hospitals several municipalities, Manchester in particular, took up places at Monsall and contributed towards the expenses of patients. Most were children with scarlet fever, though there were also smallpox cases housed in special wooden pavilions. Early death registers recorded the considerable number of child fatalities from smallpox.[8] Against many entries the words 'Not vaccinated', 'No scar', 'Faint scars' appear. There were deaths from scarlet fever and a number from typhoid. Some were from complex causes: 'dropsy after scarlatina, convulsions', 'pneumonia following fever', 'cerebellar abscess', 'abscess ankle, pericarditis, pleurisy, septicaemia, pyaemia'.

Until 1896 when Manchester Corporation took over Monsall it was under the control of the Royal Infirmary. Surviving records of the late '80s show the lengthy periods of isolation—up to ninety days for scarlet fever. Diphtheria had the highest death rate, often up to 20 per cent. Some 5 per cent of the larger numbers of scarlet fever cases were fatal, and there were child deaths also from pneumonia, meningitis, erysipelas and typhoid. Overall the yearly death rate for some 2,000 patients, including adults, was 14 per cent. Peculiar to workhouse children was a malignant form of measles, 'black measles'; of the batches of young children just out of infancy who were sent by the Unions, many died of the disease within a few days.

Bolton Isolation Hospital, opened 1883
Note the one-storeyed pavilions with covered south-facing verandahs

Increasingly neighbouring towns provided their own facilities for isolation. Some were merely converted cottages, as at Macclesfield, or a wooden shed on the fringe of a main hospital, as at Preston, but usually they were specially built and situated well away from the populated areas. The hospital in Bolton, for example, was at Bolton le Moors, and press reports on the new hospital in 1883 made a point of noting that every window had been made to open.[9] Patients were transported by ambulance brougham. Sometimes, as in Burnley, where the horses were hired from an undertaker, there were delays while they plied their normal business; the Burnley horses were frequently driven up to the hospital still attached to the empty hearse and then transferred to the ambulance![10]

Despite precautions there were occasions when children, admitted to isolation hospital with one infectious disease, contracted another during their stay. In Monsall during 1889 numbers of children who were brought in with scarlet fever contracted smallpox. By the '90s several municipalities, in consequence of similar unfortunate experiences in their fever hospitals, had opened separate smallpox institutions.

Just as some parents had in the past evaded vaccination of their children or objected to the full number of vaccination marks, so now they resisted isolation. As in the case of vaccination, publicity was used to try to convince parents of the need for prompt action. But isolation, whether at home or in hospital, brought strain and often economic loss to families. Few households could maintain the rigorous quarantine restrictions over protracted periods, extending in the case of scarlet fever to two months. Frequently they did not have the resources for the special diet and treatment prescribed during the illness or for the nourishment recommended for convalescence. Tradesmen and shopkeepers with home-based businesses were particularly hard-hit by strict sanitary regulations.[11]

There were complications of a different sort when the patient was removed to isolation hospital. The house was immediately stoved and disinfected, a procedure which rendered the family homeless for a day. The wallpaper was stripped off, on occasions as many as eleven or twelve layers were removed, and a solution of caustic soda applied, followed by a coat of whitewash.[12] Indeed, with the new techniques of the '90s portable sprays were brought in for fumigation by sulphorous acid gas. (Schools, similarly, after closure were 'smoked' and whitewashed.) Altogether the whole process could be both frightening and financially crippling for families.

Meanwhile there was danger of loss or damage to clothing and household articles, including mattresses and pillows, which were collected by covered van and put through steam disinfectors. Clothing posed great problems. It was a major source of infection; some medical officers were of the opinion that destruction was the only solution and accordingly ordered articles to be burnt.[13] Families often resisted the sanitary measures; some had only a single set of clothing, others were at pains to preserve precious garments bought at great sacrifice. Thus there was always the danger that, when a patient was removed, infected clothing would be hidden away or surreptitiously taken to a pawnshop. To medical authorities, confident of their measures of containment, such concealment was irrational and short-sighted; to many householders, on the other hand, it was their only defence against ruthless destruction or damage to cherished possessions.

When isolation facilities were first provided in a locality, parents were extremely fearful and hospitals which excluded them completely were highly unpopular. Most institutions, therefore, found it advisable to allow visits, but to take suitable precautions. As, over the years, parents were reassured both by what they saw of hospitals and by the knowledge of declining death rates their alarm subsided. By the closing years of the century a high proportion of the notified cases of scarlet fever in the larger towns were being sent to isolation hospitals. Salford alone, for example, was sending 1,000 children a year to its own hospital at Wilton, and to Monsall.[14] However, there were still boroughs, and indeed many smaller districts, which had no facilities for isolation and had to manage with such poor substitutes as providing 'carbolised oil' for rubbing over the body.

For smallpox medical authorities kept up the pressure for vaccination, which after 1871 was the responsibility of District Vaccination Officers appointed by Guardians. They were to ensure that parents availed themselves of free treatment and to provide facilities for revaccination. Despite powers of legal compulsion, however, even in the '80s there were towns where half the infants were unvaccinated. Families were warned that, whenever the disease struck, the highest proportion of deaths was of unvaccinated children.

Certain measures were taken to curb the incidence of tuberculosis, which affected children as well as adults: the inspection of cow-sheds, the prosecution of sellers of infected milk and campaigns to persuade mothers to boil milk before feeding it to children. However, action against dairymen and retailers was rarely pursued with vigour, while handbills and leaflets on child feeding had only a limited impact. Again, though medical authorities recognised that phthisis could be effectively tackled by destruction of infected sputum and the conditions which nourished it, lack of fresh air and sunlight, overcrowding and damp subsoils, they were circumscribed in their powers.

In their antiseptic approach they were particularly frustrated by ingrained habits. Hence in the long term they and other reformers looked to the schools to change attitudes and to provide, by example and training, preparation for family life. Already from the '80s in urban schools or centres there were cookery classes for girls as well as similar classes in the evening for older age groups. Stockport, as has been mentioned, was the pioneer authority in bringing in a health visitor to lecture to senior girls on Infant Hygiene, a course which was expanded to cover Infant Feeding and Management.

The large modern Board Schools which provided facilities for practical subjects were light and spacious. Ventilated, as were the new infirmaries, by the latest system of Tobin's Tubes or Sheringham Valves which carried away impurities and smells, they were healthy and provided proper playgrounds. Other schools, however, came in for criticism. Frequently voluntary schools (and for historical reasons the area had a disproportionate number, provided by the Churches) were in old and dilapidated premises where the lighting was poor and the ventilation, cloakrooms and lavatories inadequate. Some buildings had never been intended for use as schools. Outside, the playgrounds were often sited ominously close to burial grounds. Quite apart from the situation, cindered surfaces were hazardous; in winter they became a mass of black mud, in dry weather the clouds of dust which rose during children's play brought on attacks of bronchitis and conjunctivitis. The condition of external 'offices' had long been a scandal.

Everywhere the older school architecture and furniture imposed physical strain. The arrangement by which several classes shared a single big room caused hearing and eyesight problems. Moreover children in their 'standards' sat at iron-framed desks which were all of one size as though their occupants were of uniform age and stature. School furniture was seemingly indestructible, and both desks and benches, made with little regard for the human anatomy or physiology, had continued in use for decades. Hence, because pupils had to bend awkwardly, spines were twisted and shoulders contorted.

Conditions in schools as well as at home gave rise to rheumatism. Many children sat through the day in damp boots. (Clogs were said to keep the feet drier.) Wet clothes, left in dark, cold cloakrooms, were still damp when they were put on again at 'home time'. Rheumatism, itself often passed off as 'growing pains', was frequently a cause of heart disease, and of chorea, which was also associated with overpressure and affected girls particularly. Medical journals drew attention to the numerous 'little tremblers' who had been overtaxed by school work; a leading medical authority referred to the disease as 'school-made chorea'.[15] Girl pupils who had put in long hours at school were particularly at risk. In the '80s discussion of the overpressure controversy at national level led to a proposal for the provision of milk in schools. The comment of the Chief Inspector of Schools, that 'school is established for the purpose of instruction and not for the purpose of dispensing new milk', summarised the grounds of opposition to any infringement of parental responsibility.[16]

Increasingly, however, the introduction of exercise and drill drew attention to pupils who were weakly and ill clad. So long as school routine had been of the traditional sedentary type, physical deficiencies had been less obvious. At best, feeding by philanthropic agencies was spasmodic and temporary, and much education was wasted on children who were too hungry to learn.

Medical officers frequently used their powers to close schools in order to confine epidemics, though some were doubtful whether children were less infectious playing in the streets than in contact at the school. Most frequent of the school infections was measles, which travelled like lightning through infant departments. Indeed, the only child in a family was often kept at home by parents as long as possible in order to avoid common infections and contagious eruptions of the skin and scalp. In large families, however, 'mere babies' of three years were sent to school, often in all weathers and without adequate clothing. They made their way through unpaved streets, ankle-deep in mud, and sat through the day in damp footwear and clothing. Some suffered continually from colds which later developed into bronchitis and weakened their resistance to tuberculosis.

There were reports of cheerless daily routines, with the 'babies' in large classes 'drilled to listless quiet . . .'.[17] Always numbers had arrived an hour before school began. In the winter they huddled together outside and breathed on chilblained hands, especially painful on the break-up of the frost. Once in the classroom, many sat on backless gallery seats with their feet dangling. There were accidents when they fell off, and even cases of concussion of the brain. Subjected to military discipline, they spent most of the time cramped and immobile. Such an unnatural regime—'incarceration' was the term used by one woman HMI—was in dismal contrast to conditions in the one kindergarten in the area, founded in Salford in 1873 by William

Mather, of the engineering firm, and organised on Froebelian lines. Here children of two and upwards were bathed and fed on premises which included rest rooms as well as rooms for play.[18]

Apart from isolation hospitals, public provision for the sick was confined chiefly to paupers. During the latter decades of the century Unions built large workhouses including pavilion-style infirmaries. Though some came to be accepted by non-paupers, there were many in the community who were unwilling to avail themselves of their services. For most families the dangers of disease were as nothing compared with the humiliation of entering the Union hospital. Hence, as one medical officer pointed out, fathers with tuberculosis deferred treatment and stayed at home until there was no hope. Their entire families, meanwhile, were weakened by privation.[19]

Inflexible workhouse rules could be a fatal cause of delay in obtaining both medical help and outdoor relief. Moreover the latter, given principally in kind according to printed scales and consisting largely of flour and oatmeal, was often unsuitable for particular needs. Where relief was given in money, of the order of a shilling a week for each child, investigators found, not surprisingly, that children were ill nourished, and fed mostly on bread and milkless tea. In Stockport the medical officer, in his evidence before the Poor Law Commission in 1907, stated categorically that there would be no difficulty in reducing the appalling rate of infantile mortality if only he could obtain adequate food for poor mothers.[20]

Always, there were large numbers of children in the workhouses. Some were brought in emaciated and deformed; most were in need of treatment owing to malnutrition and neglect. Even in the later years of the century and well into the twentieth there were institutions with sick children in adult wards. Typical of the older workhouses was Stockport where, according to a body of medical visitors, inmates were 'packed like sardines in a tin' in buildings that were comfortless and forbidding. Here even the nursery was joyless, 'with no sign of play or merriment'. No cots were provided, and instead the infants were slung in hammocks. In the children's wards the patients, looked after by paupers, were described as 'sorry objects'. As an overflow into the female ward there were in a single bed two children with ophthalmia.[21]

In contrast, in the modern workhouse infirmaries, such as those in Salford and Chorlton, there were special children's wards. Child patients generally suffered from debility and from long-standing diseases such as rickets and tuberculosis; others were treated for infections, a variety of skin diseases as well as ulcers and abscesses. Some, diagnosed to have acute ophthalmia, were sent to the Royal Eye Hospital. Always among the child paupers there were cripples, who were provided with crutches or steel leg supports.

For the unfortunate infants who were born in workhouse lying-in wards expectation of life was low. Up to three-quarters of them would be illegitimate, and, whether they were taken out of the institution or left inside to be looked after by inmates, the death rate was high. According to one report in the major national inquiry on workhouses, the walls and floors themselves were impregnated with poisonous odours:

the very cots in which the infants lie have been previously tenanted by an incalculable succession of infants in all states of health and morbidity. It may be that human infants like chickens cannot long be aggregated together even in the most carefully devised surroundings without being injuriously affected.[22]

By the closing years of the century there were signs of a more enlightened attitude to workhouse children. It was not only that the inhumanity of massing children together and segregating them was recognised. The ill effects of proximity on large numbers of children who were enfeebled and rickety were only too clear; indeed, workhouse schools were often so scourged with epidemics that they were barely distinguishable from hospitals. Gradually Unions moved towards the establishment of pleasantly situated 'cottage homes' where children could live in small communities, family units, removed from the mental and physical atmosphere of the workhouse.

In general the high Victorian period had brought an advance in living standards, and improvements in sanitation and medical provision in the textile areas. The scale of public effort was all the time extending to cut down the causes of disease to which the young were particularly vulnerable. Yet many districts were barely touched either by official action or charitable endeavour. Everywhere the infantile mortality rate was substantially unchanged. With unfailing regularity the textile towns were among those annually listed as having one in four or one in five die before reaching the age of twelve months. For past neglect and complacency the population, in the words of one medical officer, was 'paying a tax which must be reckoned, not in pounds, shillings and pence, but in years, months and days . . .'.[23]

CONCLUSION

In the industrial past society had used its resources wastefully. Of none was this more true than its human resource, particularly the young. In the textile areas, as elsewhere, childhood ended abruptly as soon as regular work began at an age now associated with infancy. It was the scale of child labour in the steam-driven mills which was the distinctive feature of the area in the early nineteenth century. With their sharp eyes, nimble fingers and small, agile bodies children were considered indispensable to the factory regime. Long after their hours of labour were restricted they continued to combine the role of factory worker and school pupil.

It was not only juvenile workers who were at risk. Within the communities the consequences of industrialisation blighted young lives often from the moment of birth. In this, the first large-scale area of urbanisation, the most sinister effects of early death and disease were for long masked by the flow of incomers. By the later years of the century the harvest of neglect could no longer be ignored. The extent of physical deterioration was a terrible indictment of the old industrial environment; with two-thirds of the population now urbanised it was a portent of degeneration in the nation as a whole.

In the history of childhood, therefore, the region is unique. Here in the early nineteenth century were some of the worst industrial conditions under which children were pitilessly exploited. However, it was here also that the very scale of the problem roused the social conscience. Textile children were the first to be safeguarded both in their hours of labour and in their conditions of work. They were the first for whom school attendance was a requisite of employment.

When, some thirty and forty years later, similar regulations were extended to the labyrinthine pot banks, to the small unwholesome workshops and dens of sweated labour, the textile factories were contrasted for their model conditions and the half-time system was praised for its efficiency in promoting literacy. Over the nation as a whole, children in the Victorian period were more effectively protected in the textile mills than in small-scale industry or agriculture.

The cause of ailing children roused philanthropic effort. Their need stirred imagination, and charity on their behalf could be justified on the grounds that it helped those who were incapable of helping themselves. Thus humanitarian concern, expressed in the foundation of voluntary institutions, dispensaries, hospitals and other societies, afforded help to the weakly and debilitated.

The scale of charity, however, was quite inadequate to the task. It was, for example, only in the largest centres that special medical provision was made for children or, apart from minor charities, for childbirth. Nor did the numerous self-help organisations touch major sections of the community. Many catered only for workers and excluded their families; others, which provided limited relief, were most popularly supported for the purpose of death insurance; only exceptionally did they afford help in childbirth, a perilous event which would have jeopardised the whole basis of their finances. As for public intervention, positive action was confined to protection against the most dangerous and degrading conditions.

On the medical front firm action had been taken to stamp out one disease and one disease only, smallpox, a traditional scourge which had exacted a high toll of the young. Here the State had intervened decisively. There was no comparable attack on other diseases. For children who came through the perils of infancy there was, by the latter years of the century, a better chance of survival in areas where health measures were vigorously carried out and where, in particular, epidemics were quickly brought under control. Some children were able to benefit from curative and reparative medicine, though often their recovery was impaired by lack of food and care during convalescence. Others, less fortunate, received no medical help.

Consequently there were many who were rarely free of pain, who had 'crippled systems' and who were doomed to become chronic invalids. There was, therefore, at the end of the century not only immense infant mortality, a scale of human wastage comparable with that we ourselves associate with natural disasters, with civil strife in distant continents or with conditions in the most backward regions of the Third World; there was also in many survivors a legacy from childhood of weakness and debility which brought premature death and consequently a new cycle of poverty and privation to the next generation.

The full realisation of the significance of the child as 'the product of the last generation and the producer of the next'[1] came with the impact of the statistics of a decreasing birthrate and the revelation of physical decline at the turn of the century.[2] In particular there was consternation at the number of youths from the industrial towns who were judged to be unfit for military service. In Manchester alone, of over 11,000 would-be recruits for the Boer campaign in 1899, only 25 per cent were accepted.[3] For some time eugenic spokesmen had drawn attention to the dangers of social deterioration. Their views were now brought into sharper focus.

War time revelations confirmed the warnings of dispensary physicians, accustomed daily to treating children who were enfeebled and deformed. From the dispensary associated with the Children's Hospital Ashby said he could produce, 'so as to account for every one of those 8,000 recruits who were rejected, 8,000 children now in Manchester at quite a young age who are rickety and unfit to make soldiers, or anything else because of their improper nurture and improper care'.[4]

The closer children lived to the centre of towns the worse was their physique. At the age of thirteen the boy from the Salford slum was four inches shorter and sixteen pounds lighter than his fellow in a good working-class neighbourhood.[5] In Rochdale—not by industrial standards an unhealthy town—it took, according to the calculations of the Vicar, a former headmaster of Clifton, three schoolboys to equal the weight of two public-school boys of the same age.[6] In the worst urban areas expectation of life for infants was only half that of the country as a whole. As the medical officer of Manchester pointed out, the root of the problem was malnutrition; 'in order to get good soldiers you must rear good children and see that they are adequately fed'.[7]

In the past many had been content to ignore the death toll and had pointed out from examples of daily life that children were apparently sufficiently resistant and adaptive to thrive in almost any conditions. With a spawning child population life had been held cheap. It had been accepted that feeble children would die young, and on evolutionary grounds early attrition could be regarded simply as part of the 'purifying process' of nature by which only the fittest survived.

Voluntary endeavour had touched on some of the worst aspects of disease. It had also indicated the extent of unrelieved suffering and human tragedy, the thousands of deaths which were preventable and the weakness of many survivors whose development was arrested and whose capacities were curtailed. The effects were perpetuated in offspring predisposed to disease. Despite the extent of voluntary effort and the widening scope of official action, it was clear that life was being wasted on a prodigal scale and that the seeds of national degeneration were sown during infancy and childhood.

In the early industrial era Ferriar in Manchester had warned of the dangers of neglecting children's basic requirements—regular, nutritious meals and fresh air. Again and again in the nineteenth century doctors had stressed that it was food rather than drugs that many young patients needed and that, particularly at the convalescent stage, suitable nourishment would have rendered further assistance unnecessary. Yet many were denied the very sustenance which would have given them a prospect of health. If only, in the words of the dialect writer Edwin Waugh, men (and, he might have added, their children) had been machines, how carefully then would they have been 'oiled and tended and mended . . .'.[8]

Not until the early twentieth century were there palliative measures to enable weakly children to benefit from a period in open-air institutions where they could be built up over a period with nourishing food. Even then the move was tentative and places were so scarce that the dilemma of the examining doctor was one of selection. As one medical officer put it, there were few children in his town who would not have benefited from several months in the country air. Of many children presented to him, all he could say was, 'This child needs a new home; I'm sorry I can't recommend it.'[9]

From the first decade of the new century the State was to embark on a programme of preventive medicine, the diagnosis and treatment of children's ailments and defects before they developed into major disease and disabilities. It was simultaneously to adopt a more enlightened and humanitarian approach to the whole problem of children with handicaps. Above all, it was to take the first cautious move towards provision at public expense of regular nourishment at school.

In the new era of 'collective humanism' there were efforts to dispel the worst influences of the old industrial environment and to give a measure of protection to families beset by severe privation. By the second decade of the century the State was finally to renounce the concept of the child as a wage-earner and to extend the defined age of childhood well into adolescence;[10] it was in due course to evolve a new perception of responsibility, unequivocably expressed in the words of an inter-war report, 'What a wise and good parent would desire for his own children, that a nation must desire for all children'.[11]

In the long term the problem of juvenile welfare was a psychological and social one affecting not only children but parents and communities. It was not merely a question of extending medical observation and treatment or of providing milk and meals. It was a matter of securing the support and co-operation of adults by a more sympathetic approach, of attempting to understand the grounds of popular fears and inhibitions. Above all, it was a case of eliminating the root causes of disease by measures of social improvement and, in particular, of relieving pressures at the most critical stages of family life: of child-bearing and child-rearing.

In the early years of the nineteenth century the industrial districts of the North-west represented an alarming urban phenomenon. The dense mill towns had sprung up suddenly. To outsiders they appeared as new territories, raw 'frontier' areas, their populations as unknown masses, easily moved to violence and crime. Visitors came to marvel at the machinery, others to record descriptions of their operators as though they were dwellers on a different planet. Even in the mid-Victorian era the region was likened to one of the most recent colonies for its energy and rudeness. Underlying all were fears for the moral and social order.

Gradually apprehensions subsided as new generations were tamed and trained to accept factory routine, as with speedier communications the region became less remote and as prosperity eased social tensions. Amid the relentless advance of urbanisation the area ceased to be exceptional save in the scale and tradition of its industry and in the distinctness of its culture.

Today in the North-west textile manufacturing is barely a shadow of its former strength. The once familiar clogs and shawls, the fustian trousers and cloth caps have become a part of folk memory. Still visible on the landscape, however, are many of the contemporary buildings. The Victorian town halls, built at the centres of the communities and recently cleansed of their grime and dirt, stand in their original splendour. The surviving mills, once so closely linked with family fortunes, now have different sights and sounds within, but remain in their physical exteriors symbolic of the harshness and vitality of their age.

Some aspects of life associated with the latter belong wholly to the past. It is not merely a temporal but a psychological gulf that separates us from the era when the factory regime relied on child workers and when malnutrition and mortality were to be found on a scale now associated with underdeveloped countries. The old exhortations to thrift and sobriety, cleanliness and orderly habits have a quaintly missionary flavour in our own day. Less remote from our observation and experience perhaps are some of the physical conditions which persisted long into our own century, the squalid streets and degrading sanitation and, among individuals, habits and attitudes bred of insecurity which survived into old age.

Some of the issues which exercised people in the industrial past have a striking modernity: the dilemmas and practical problems created by the employment of mothers and the conflicts on domestic values. Always the greatest burden is on large families with young children and under the starker conditions of the Victorian age, illness, accident or misfortune could have catastrophic effects and bring households to breaking point. From our own times we can perhaps view with more sympathy than could some contemporaries the reaction to such strains, and temper our judgement accordingly.

NOTES

INTRODUCTION

1 *Educational Reconstruction*, 1943, Cmd 6458, p. 3.
2 Peter Laslett, *The World we have lost*, London, 1971, pp. 108–10.
3 Daniel Defoe, *A Tour through the whole Island of Great Britain* (1724–26), London, 1966, II, p. 195. *Note:* throughout, bracketed dates are those of first publication.
4 Thomas Percival 'Observations on the State of Population in Manchester and other adjacent Places', *Essays Medical, Philosophical, and Experimental*, London, 1789, II, p. 42.
5 A. P. Wadsworth and J. De Lacy Mann, *The Cotton Trade and Industrial Lancashire, 1600–1780*, Manchester, 1965, p. 405.
6 C. Stella Davies, ed., *A History of Macclesfield*, Manchester, 1968, p. 142.
7 Robert Roberts, 'Class development in an industrial society', *Eccles and District History Society Lectures*, 1972–73, p. 6.
8 Edward Baines, *History of the Cotton Manufacture in Great Britain* (1835), London, 1966, p. 372.
9 Charles Smith, 'Stockport in the Age of Reform', unpublished, 1938, p. 51, Stockport Public Library. (Henceforth S.P.L.)
10 *Report*, 1845, p. 10.
11 P.P. 1839, XVI, p. 62.

I TRANSITION FROM THE OLD ORDER, 1780–1833

I CHILDREN AND INDUSTRY

1 Daniel Defoe, *A Tour*, p. 189.
2 *Ibid.*, p. 261.
3 Thomas Percival, *Essays*, II, p. 62.
4 Poor Relief Notebooks of Ann Eckroyd, Little Marsden, Farrer Papers, Manchester Central Library. (Henceforth M.C.L.)
5 Butterworth Diary, 6 May 1830, Oldham Public Library. (Henceforth O.P.L.)
6 W. H. Chaloner, ed., *The Autobiography of Samuel Bamford*, London, 1967, I, pp. 104–5.
7 Diary extracts in W. Bennett, *History of Burnley*, Burnley, 1948, III, Appendix II.
8 P.P. 1835, XIII, p. 7.

9   Poor Relief Notebooks, Little Marsden.
10   *Ibid.*, Township of Burnley.
11   William Rowbottom, 'The Chronology or Annals of Oldham', 1 January 1795, O.P.L.
12   P. E. Razzell and R. W. Wainwright, eds., *The Victorian Working Class. Selections from Letters to the Morning Chronicle*, 1849–50, London, 1973, p. 180.
13   Moses Heap of Rossendale, 'My Life and Times' (1824–1913), unpublished, p. 4, Rawtenstall Public Library.
14   Stalybridge figures taken from Archdeacon Rushton's Visitation Returns for Stalybridge, M.C.L.
15   J. Aikin, *A Description of the Country from Thirty to Forty Miles round Manchester*, London, 1795, p. 3.
16   Frederick Engels, *The Condition of the Working Class in England* (1845), London, 1969, p. 90.
17   P. E. Razzell and R. W. Wainwright, eds., *The Victorian Working Class*, p. 172.
18   E. J. Hobsbawm, *Industry and Empire*, Harmondsworth, 1969, p. 56.
19   John Fielden, *The Curse of the Factory System* (1836), London, 1967, p. 12.
20   Butterworth Diary, 15 August 1836, O.P.L.
21   G. H. Tupling, 'Economic History of Rossendale', *Chetham Society*, LXXXVI, 1927, p. 217.
22   Robert Murray, 'Quarry Bank Mill, the medical service', *British Journal of Industrial Medicine*, XVI, 1959, p. 66.
23   'Memoranda of Quarry Bank Mill from its commencement about 1784', unpublished, p. 27, Quarry Bank Mill.
24   M.C.L.
25   George Unwin, *Samuel Oldknow and the Arkwrights*, London, 1924, p. 170.
26   'Memoranda', p. 17.
27   P.P. 1816, III, pp. 178 *et seq.* Backbarrow was near Ulverston.
28   A. P. Wadsworth and J. De Lacy Mann, *The Cotton Trade*, p. 408.
29   Moses Heap of Rossendale, 'My Life and Times', p. 1.
30   C. Aspin, *Lancashire, the First Industrial Society*, Helmshore, 1969, p. 36.
31   P.P. 1816, III, p. 54.
32   Nassau W. Senior, *Letters on the Factory Act as it affects the Cotton Manufacture*, London, 1837, p. 27.
33   P.P. 1816, III, p. 197.
34   *Ibid.*, p. 212.
35   W. H. Chaloner, ed., *The Autobiography of Samuel Bamford*, I, p. 54.
36   Thomas Henry, 'Observations on bills of mortality in Manchester and Salford', *Memoirs of the Literary and Philosophical Society of Manchester*, III, 1790, p. 171.
37   The term is used of incomers.
38   Discussion of incidence of relationship, M. M. Edwards and R. Lloyd Jones, 'N. J. Smelser and the cotton factory family: a reassessment', N. B. Harte and K. G. Ponting, eds., *Textile History and Economic History*, Manchester, 1973, p. 315.
39   P.P. 1833, XX, p. 42.
40   Frances Collier, *The Family Economy of the Working Classes in the Cotton Industry, 1784–1833*, Manchester, 1964, p. 60.
41   *Ibid.*, p. 61.
42   C. H. Lee, *A Cotton Enterprise, 1795–1840. A History of M'Connel & Kennedy, Fine Cotton Spinners*, Manchester, 1972, p. 124.

43 Quoted in Frances Collier, *The Family Economy of the Working Classes*, p. 20.
44 See p. 50.
45 The outbreak and investigation are described in Anon, 'The putrid fever at Robert Peel's Radcliffe Mills', *Notes and Queries*, CCIII, 1958, pp. 28 *et seq*., and A. Meiklejohn, ed., 'Outbreak of fever in cotton mills at Radcliffe 1784', *Journal of Industrial Medicine*, XVI, 1959, pp. 68 *et seq*. (There was, in fact, some doubt as to the severity of the outbreak.)

II CHILDREN AND THE ENVIRONMENT

1 *Proceedings of the Board of Health in Manchester*, 7 January 1796.
2 Best flour was often twice the price of 'ordinary' flour. The 'hard cakes' are described in James Bradley, *Reminiscences in the Life of Joshua Bradley* (1904), Ilkley, 1974, p. 32.
3 Moses Heap of Rossendale, 'My Life and Times', p. 6.
4 Frances Collier, *The Family Economy of the Working Classes*, p. 53.
5 John Ferriar, *Medical Histories and Reflections*, London, 1810, I, p. 167.
6 *Ibid.*, II, p. 229.
7 *Proceedings of the Board of Health*, 7 January 1796.
8 John Ferriar, *Medical Histories*, II, p. 233.
9 *Proceedings of the Board of Health*, 2 July 1801.
10 *Ibid.*, 10 December 1801.
11 Both this and the following proposal were taken from Percival's 'Heads of Resolutions', 25 January 1796.
12 P.P. 1816, III, p. 267. For 1802 Act see Appendix II.
13 Henry Gaulter, *Origin and Progress of the Malignant Cholera in Manchester*, London, 1833, p. 7.
14 *Annual Report of the Stockport Sunday School*, 1832–33, p. 5.
15 Henry Gaulter, *Origin and Progress of the Malignant Cholera*, p. 137.
16 Minutes of the Special Board of Health, Manchester, 17 August 1832. Within six weeks of the first appearance of cholera ninety-four deaths had been recorded.
17 *Ibid.*, 3 September 1832. Events described in the *Times*, 5 September 1832.

III CHILD MORTALITY AND DISEASE

1 Thomas Percival, *Essays*, II, p. 41.
2 W. M. Spencer, ed., *Burial Register, 1790–1812, Parochial Chapelry of Colne*, Colne, 1968, pp. vii–viii, 159.
3 Thomas Percival, *Essays*, II, p. 65.
4 John Roberton, *Observations on the Mortality and Physical Management of Children*, London, 1827, p. 38. Roberton became surgeon at the Lying-in Hospital in 1827.
5 Thomas Percival, *Essays*, II, p. 79.
6 *Ibid.*, pp. 75–6. The method was of inoculation with fluid from a vesicle.
7 *Ibid.*, p. 75.
8 *Ibid.*, p. 79.
9 *Ibid.*, p. 22.
10 Registers in Salford Public Library.
11 John Roberton, *Observations*, p. 58.

12 *Ibid.*, p. 80.
13 Archdeacon Rushton's Visitation Returns for Blackburn, M.C.L.
14 P.P. 1816, III, p. 207.
15 *Ibid.*, p. 198.
16 Hurst Collection, VI, p. 63, S.P.L.

IV FAMILY SELF-HELP

1 Ben Brierley, *Home Memories and Recollections of a Life*, Manchester, 1886, p. 3.
2 C. Stella Davies, *North Country Bred*, London, 1963, p. 18.
3 P.P. 1842, XVII, p. 163.
4 E. M. Brockbank, *Sketches of the Lives and Work of the Honorary Medical Staff of the Manchester Infirmary, 1752–1830*, Manchester, 1904, p. 14.
5 Charles White, *A Treatise on the Management of Pregnant and Lying-in Women*, London, 1777, pp. 4–6.
6 *Ibid.*, p. 118.
7 Series of Bills of Mortality in Archdeacon Rushton's Visitation Returns for Blackburn.
8 William Brockbank, 'Historical Fools', unpublished, p. 18.
9 *Lancet*, 19 June 1841, p. 424.
10 Elizabeth Gaskell, *Mary Barton* (1848), London, 1966, p. 26.
11 John Roberton, *Observations*, p. 80.
12 George Eliot. *Felix Holt*, Edinburgh and London, n. d., pp. 203-4.
13 Between 9*d* and 1*s* per pound between 1810 and 1819. Frances Collier, *The Family Economy*, p. 62.
14 Moses Heap of Rossendale, 'My Life and Times', p. 4.
15 For example, Vicar of Smallbridge (describing Wardle), 20 July 1843, National Society Letter Files.
16 For example, school founded by hand-loom weavers in Little Marsden, 1832. Marjorie Cruickshank, 'A Lancashire handloom weavers' school', *Journal of Educational Administration and History*, IX, 1979, pp. 15–18.
17 A. P. Wadsworth, 'The first Manchester Sunday Schools', *Bulletin of the John Rylands' Library*, XXXIII, 1951, p. 310.
18 P.P. 1816, III, p. 268.
19 W. E. Axon, *Annals of Manchester*, Manchester, 1886, p. 28. Already in Oldham there had been military-style processions of Sunday school children marshalled by a local doctor. C. E. Ward, 'Education as Social Control. Sunday Schools in Oldham *c.* 1750–1850', unpublished M.A. thesis, University of Lancaster, 1975, p. 31.
20 *A Report of the Present State of the Stockport Sunday School*, 1806, p. 20.
21 Frances Collier, *The Family Economy*, p. 40.
22 Moses Heap of Rossendale, 'My Life and Times', pp. 4–5.
23 Butterworth Diary, 10 June 1830.
24 Link between early industrialism and the new Dissent described in A. D. Gilbert, *Religion and Society in Industrial England*, London, 1976, pp. 61 *et seq*. It is recorded of the home of Edwin Waugh (born in Rochdale 1817 of a family with strong Wesleyan associations) that among the few books kept on the window sill was Colpepper's *Herbal*. Edwin Waugh, *Lancashire Sketches*, first series, Manchester, 1892, p. xxii.

25 Arthur Newsholme, *Fifty Years in Public Health*, London, 1935, p. 24.
26 'An address to the inhabitants of Preston and the Neighbourhood especially to Parents and Masters from the Committee of the National School', 24 January 1815, Lancashire County Record Office.
27 R. H. Greg, *The Factory Question considered in relation to its effects on the Health and Morals of those Employed in Factories*, London, 1837, p. 41.
28 P.P. 1834, XIX, p. 598.
29 *Report of the Sick and Funeral Society belonging to Bennett Street Sunday School*, 1843, p. 15; Funeral Registers, German Street Sunday School, 1829–32, M.C.L. The following paragraph draws on these sources.
30 James Black, 'Bolton and its neighbourhood, 1837', *Transactions of the Provincial Medical and Surgical Association*, 1837, p. 183.

V PHILANTHROPIC ENDEAVOUR

1 W. H. Chaloner, ed., *The Autobiography of Samuel Bamford*, I, p. 75.
2 T. Battye, *Strictures upon the Churchwardens and Overseers of Manchester*, Manchester, 1801, p. 62.
3 *Ibid.*, p. 77.
4 *Ibid.*, p. 80.
5 *Ibid.*, pp. 84–5.
6 T. S. Ashton, *An Eighteenth Century Industrialist. Peter Stubs of Warrington, 1756–1806*, Manchester, 1961, p. 28.
7 Prescription Book, Quarry Bank Mill, M.C.L.
8 'Rules and Orders', 9 June 1790.
9 *Report of the Manchester Lying-in Hospital*, 1795-6, p. 2.
10 *Report of St Mary's Hospital and Dispensary*, 1877, p. 14.
11 *First Annual Report of the Burnley Ladies' Charity*, 1820–21, p. 4.
12 Edward Baines, *History, Directory and Gazetteer of the County Palatine of Lancaster* (1824), Newton Abbot, 1968, I, p. 536.
13 Minute Book of the Bolton Dispensary, 5 January 1816.
14 James Black, 'Bolton and its neighbourhood', p. 209.
15 *Bolton Chronicle*, 26 March 1831.
16 James Kay-Shuttleworth, 'The Moral and Physical Condition of the Working Classes of Manchester in 1832', *Four Periods of Public Education*, London, 1862, pp. 42–3.
17 'Rules and Orders of the Public Infirmary, Manchester', 1752.
18 Admission Register.
19 John Aikin, *Thoughts on Hospitals*, London, 1771, p. 9.
20 *Ibid.*, p. 18.
21 Minutes of Weekly Board Meeting, Manchester Infirmary, 20 February 1791.
22 The source on the use of cod-liver oil is a letter by Robert Darbey. Thomas Percival, *Essays*, II, pp. 357, 361–2.
23 W. H. Brindley, 'Thomas Percival', *Memoirs of the Manchester Literary and Philosophical Society*, LXXIV, 1939–41, p. 64.
24 'Rules', 79 and 80.
25 Minutes of Weekly Board Meeting, 16 September 1799, 27 February 1804.
26 *Ibid.*, 8 September 1800.
27 *Ibid.*, 2 March 1801.

28 P.P. 1816, III, pp. 299–300.
29 Hurst Collection, VI, p. 63.
30 *Fifth Annual Report*, p. 5.
31 F. S. Stancliffe, *Manchester Royal Eye Hospital, 1814–1964*, Manchester, 1964, p. 11.
32 Early reports are missing. Resolution to open a dispensary was reported in the *Manchester Guardian*, 3 January 1829. Three months later there were forty patients; *Manchester Guardian*, 11 April 1829.
33 *Report of the Committee of the Salford and Pendleton Dispensary*, 1838, p. 7.
34 James Kay-Shuttleworth, *Four Periods of Public Education*, pp. 41–3.

II THE FACTORY AGE, 1833–70

I CHILDREN AND INDUSTRY

1 P. E. Razzell and R. W. Wainwright, eds., *The Victorian Working Class*, p. 182.
2 *Stockport Advertiser*, 15 November 1822.
3 *Replies of Sir Charles Shaw to Lord Ashley M.P. regarding the Education, and Moral and Physical Condition of the Working Classes*, London, 1843, p. 7.
4 Described in Marjorie Cruickshank, 'The Anglican revival and education: a study of school expansion in the cotton manufacturing areas of north-west England, 1840–1850', *Northern History*, XV, 1979, pp. 176–9.
5 'Report on the Condition of the Working Classes in an Extensive Manufacturing District in 1834, 1835 and 1836', *Papers of the Manchester Statistical Society*, 1838, p. 14.
6 At Ashton Parish Church the average percentage of grooms who signed with their marks in 1763, 1783 and 1803 was 42·8; for the years 1823, 1833 and 1843 the percentage was 85·1. P.P. 1844, XVII, Appendix, p. 86. At Chorley Parish Church, of the marriages between 1800 and 1825, 24·7 per cent of grooms signed with their mark and of those between 1831 and 1835, 63·9 per cent of grooms. Percentages calculated from statistics in K. P. C. Thorne, 'Development of Education in Chorley and District from 1800 to 1902', unpublished M. Litt. thesis, University of Lancaster, 1970, p. 134.
7 Quoted in *Annual Report of the Manchester Clinical Hospital*, 1868, p. 14.
8 1851 Census Returns, Rossendale valley villages and of Bollington, Cheshire. Also shown in Owen Ashmore, 'Low Moor, Clitheroe. A nineteenth century factory community', *Transactions of the Lancashire and Cheshire Antiquarian Society*, LXXIII and LXXIV, 1963–64, p. 148.
9 *Report of the British Association for the Advancement of Science*, 1842, Transactions, p. 93.
10 C. Stella Davies, *North Country Bred*, p. 18.
11 Andrew Ure, *The Philosophy of Manufactures* (1835), London, 1967, p. 352; Rhodes Boyson, *The Ashworth Cotton Enterprise*, Oxford, 1970, p. 92.
12 P.P. 1833, XXI, p. 206.
13 P.P. 1843, XVI, pp. 205–7.
14 W. Cooke Taylor, *Notes of a Tour in the Manufacturing Districts of Lancashire* (1842), London, 1968, p. 239.
15 Nassau W. Senior, *Letters on the Factory Act*, p. 15.
16 P.P. 1834, XX, p. D1 16.

17   A. Combe, *Principles of Physiology*, London, 1834, p. 159. Quoted in W. H. Hutt, 'The factory system of the early nineteenth century', in F. A. Hayek, ed., *Capitalism and the Historians*, London, 1954, p. 177.

18   John Fielden, *The Curse of the Factory System*, p.xlii; R. H. Greg, *The Factory Question*, p. 73.

19   P.P. 1833, XX, p. D1 33.

20   P.P. 1834, XX, p. D1 169.

21   Adam Rushton, *My Life as a Farmer's Boy, Factory Lad and Preacher*, Manchester, 1909, p. 28.

22   William Dodd, *The Factory System Illustrated* (1842), London, 1968, p. 166.

23   P.P. 1834, XX, p. D1 296.

24   P.P. 1862, XLIII, p. 99.

25   Moses Heap of Rossendale, 'My Life and Times', p. 3.

26   P.P. 1843, XIV, pp. B14–5.

27   *Hansard*, House of Commons, Third Series, 73, 1844, col. 1238–9.

28   P.P. 1835, XIII, p. 186.

29   P.P. 1834, XIX, p. 124.

30   See p. 36.

31   Edward Baines, *History of the Cotton Manufacture*, p. 462.

32   Moses Heap of Rossendale, 'My Life and Times', p. 2.

33   P.P. 1842, XXXV, p. 16.

34   C. G. Carus, *The King of Saxony's Journey through England and Scotland in the Year 1844*, London, 1846, p. 258.

35   P.P. 1862, XXII, p. 639.

36   Quoted in the *Stockport Advertiser*, 10 March 1832.

37   Edward Baines, *History of the Cotton Manufacture*, p. 454.

38   See Appendix II.

II CHILDREN AND THE ENVIRONMENT

1   Nassau W. Senior, *Letters on the Factory Act*, p. 40; Andrew Ure, *The Philosophy of Manufactures*, p. 301.

2   Samuel Bamford, *Walks in South Lancashire* (1844), Hassocks, 1972, pp. 32–3.

3   P.P. 1833, XXI, p. 197.

4   Adam Rushton, *My Life*, p. 82.

5   G. Greaves, 'Our sewer rivers', *Transactions of the Manchester Statistical Society*, 1865–66, pp. 50–1.

6   F. A. Todd, 'Condition of the Working Class in Preston, 1790–1855', unpublished M.Litt. thesis, University of Lancaster, 1972, p. 117.

7   P.P. 1846, XXXII, p. 332.

8   P.P. 1844, XVII, Appendix, p. 59.

9   P.P. 1845, XVIII, Appendix II, p. 31.

10   *Ibid.*, p. 323.

11   Elizabeth Gaskell, *Mary Barton*, p. 67.

12   Adrian Alker, 'The Social Pathology of Wigan, 1800–1850', unpublished M.A. thesis, University of Lancaster, 1971, pp. 19, 22.

13   P.P. 1866, XIX, p. 1v.

14   William Lee, *Report to the General Board of Health on a Preliminary Inquiry into the Sewerage, Drainage, and Supply of Water and the Sanitary Condition of the Inhabitants of*

Bacup, London, 1849, p. 7.

15   P.P. 1845, XVIII, Appendix II, pp. 351, 409.

16   *Ibid.*, p. 100.

17   Lester Burney, *Cross Street Chapel Schools, Manchester, 1734–1942*, Manchester, 1977, pp. 8–11.

18   P.P. 1845, XVIII, Appendix II, p. 329.

19   *Ibid.*, p. 28.

20   P.P. 1840, XXIII, p. 14.

21   James Kay-Shuttleworth, *Four Periods of Public Education*, pp. 100–1.

22   National Society Letter Files, for example, of St James's, Clitheroe, St John's, Smallbridge, near Rochdale.

23   William Neild, 'Comparative statement of the income and expenditure of certain families of the working classes in Manchester and Dukinfield, in the years 1836 and 1841', *Journal of the Statistical Society of London*, IV, 1841, pp. 321–3. Though none of the families was depressed by unemployment, the majority of them had in 1841, according to modern calculation, a diet so low in calories and protein that resistance to disease was diminished; J. C. McKenzie, 'The composition, and nutritional value of diets in Manchester and Dukinfield, 1841', *Lancashire and Cheshire Antiquarian Society*, LXXII, 1962, pp. 138–9.

24   *Second Report of the Manchester and Salford Education Aid Society*, 1866, p. 7.

25   'Report on the Condition of the Working Classes', *Papers of the Manchester Statistical Society*, 1838, p. 7.

26   William Ranger, *Report to the General Board of Health on a Preliminary Inquiry into the Sewerage, Drainage and Supply of Water and Sanitary Condition of the Inhabitants of Dukinfield*, London, 1856, p. 10.

27   Quoted by Peter Gaskell, *Artisans and Machinery* (1836), London, 1968, p. 175.

28   *Annual Report of the Medical Officer of Health*, Rochdale, 1913, p. 17.

29   Almost twice as many grooms as brides were able to sign their names in registration districts of the North-west during the 1840s, e.g. P.P. 1841, VI, p. 12.

30   W. D. Husband, 'Infant Mortality', *Transactions of the National Association for the Promotion of Social Science*, 1864, p. 507.

31   Preston samples in Michael Anderson, *Family Structure in Nineteenth Century Lancashire*, London, 1974, p. 71. The author has investigated 1841 and 1851 Census Returns for Rossendale villages: Bacup, Lumb, Newchurch.

32   R. Burr-Litchfield, 'The family and the mill: cotton mill work, family work patterns and fertility in mid-Victorian Stockport', in Anthony S. Wohl, ed., *The Victorian Family*, London, 1978, p. 191.

33   P.P. 1842, XXXV, p. 199.

34   P.P. 1842, XVII, p. 212.

35   Criticisms in W. D. Husband, 'Infant Mortality', p. 505. The author has taken evidence from 'Abstracts' in *Registrar General's Reports*, 1858–68.

36   E. B., 'Present State of Education in Manchester and Salford' 1864, Scrapbook of Edward Brotherton, M.C.L.

37   *Instructions from the Central Board of the Children's Employment Commission to the Sub-commissioners*, London, 1840, p. 10.

38   P.P. 1862, XXII, p. 654; P.P. 1864, XXVIII, p. 456.

39   John Leigh and Ner Gardiner, *History of the Cholera in Manchester in 1849*, Manchester, 1850, p. 22.

40 *Ibid.*, p. 26.
41 In Manchester and Salford there were 1,375 deaths out of 10,000 cases of scarlet fever, *Lancet*, 23 July 1864, p. 102.
42 P.P. 1863, XXV, p. 301.
43 P.P. 1842, XXXV, p. 16.
44 P.P. 1864, XXII, p. 611.
45 P.P. 1842, XXXV, p. 295.
46 David Chadwick, 'On the Social and Educational Statistics of Manchester and Salford', *Transactions of the Manchester Statistical Society*, 1861–62, pp. 13 *et seq.*
47 Mary Brigg, 'Life in East Lancashire, 1856–60. A newly discovered diary of John O'Neil (John Ward), weaver, of Clitheroe', *Transactions of the Historic Society of Lancashire and Cheshire*, CXX, 1968, p. 104.
48 P.P. 1852, XI, p. 351.
49 *Lancet*, 11 July 1857, pp. 43–4.
50 *Ibid.*, 4 July 1857, p. 4.
51 W. Osler, *The Principles and Practice of Medicine*, London, 1913, pp. 730–1.
52 H. C. Oats, 'Inquiry into the Educational and other Conditions of a District in Ancoats', *Transactions of the Manchester Statistical Society*, 1865–66, p. 3.
53 Shaftesbury's views noted in *Annual Report of the Stockport Ragged School*, 1877, p. 1.

III CHILD MORTALITY AND DISEASE

1 Peter Gaskell, *Artisans and Machinery*, p. 114.
2 P.P. 1845, XVIII, Appendix II, pp. 357–8.
3 *Ibid.*, pp. 415–19.
4 George Greaves, 'Our Sewer Rivers', *Transactions of the Manchester Statistical Society*, 1865–66, p. 41.
5 P.P. 1844, XVII, Appendix, p. 37.
6 P.P. 1845, XVIII, Appendix II, p. 54.
7 *Ibid.*, p. 660.
8 Report of M.O.H., 1873–74, *City of Manchester Proceedings of the Council*, 1 April 1874, pp. 190–2.
9 P. E. Razzell and R. W. Wainwright, eds., *The Victorian Working Class*, p. 179.
10 George Greaves, 'Observations on Some of the Causes of Infanticide', *Transactions of the Manchester Statistical Society*, 1862–63, p. 9.
11 Coroners' records, 'Registers of Death in Stockport', 1851–56, S.P.L.
12 P.P. 1847–8, XXV, p. xxv. William Farr was compiler of abstracts in the Registrar General's office.
13 George Greaves, 'Observations on Some of the Causes of Infanticide', p. 11.
14 P.P. 1841, VI, p. 381.
15 *Stockport Advertiser*, 7 January 1842.
16 *Annual Report of the Manchester Clinical Hospital*, 1857, p. 30.
17 P.P. 1839, XVI, p. 65.
18 P.P. 1861, XVIII, p. 329.
19 P. E. Razzell and R. W. Wainwright, eds., *The Victorian Working Class*, p. 181.
20 *Dr Ballard's Report upon the Sanitary Condition of the Registration District of Bolton, Lancashire, and particularly upon its high Infant Mortality*, London 1871, p. 9.
21 *Annual Report of the Manchester Clinical Hospital*, 1860, pp. 18–19.
22 P.P. 1844, XVII, Appendix, p. 77.

23 *Ibid.*, Appendix, p. 80.
24 P.P. 1845, XVIII, Appendix, II, pp. 63–4.
25 John Hatton, *Lecture on the Sanitary Condition of Chorlton-upon-Medlock*, Manchester and Salford Sanitary Association, 1854, p. 29.
26 P.P. 1845, XVIII, Appendix II, p. 64.
27 P.P. 1842, XIX, p. 280.
28 Elizabeth Gaskell, *Mary Barton*, p. 58.
29 Register Book of Interment, General Burial Ground, Rusholme Road, Chorlton Row, M.C.L. (At this period the burial ground still served an extensive factory area.)
30 Elizabeth Longford, *Victoria R.I.*, London, 1964, p. 452.
31 Register Book of Interment, Rusholme Road, September–December 1835.
32 P.P. 1873, XX, p. 224.
33 P.P. 1860, XXIX, p. 235.
34 M. A. Baines, 'On the Prevention of Excessive Infantile Mortality', *Transactions of the Manchester Statistical Society*, 1868–69, p. 16.
35 *British Medical Journal*, 12 March 1864, p. 293.
36 J. A. V. Chapple and Arthur Pollard, eds., *The Letters of Mrs Gaskell*, Manchester, 1966, p. 13.
37 P.P. 1870, XVI, p. 218.
38 P.P. 1861, XVI, p. 444.
39 P.P. 1843, XII, pp. 235–7.
40 Sample Surveys (1831–40), Register Book of Interment, Rusholme Road.

IV FAMILY SELF-HELP

1 Report of M.O. of Heaton Norris, Stockport, to the Board of Guardians, Poor Law Union Papers, September, 1841, S.P.L.
2 10 October 1853, Coroners' records, 'Register of Deaths in Stockport', 1851–56.
3 P.P. 1845, XVIII, Appendix II, p. 412.
4 *Lancet*, 11 December 1841, p. 391.
5 John L. West, *The Taylors of Lancashire, Bone-setters and Doctors, 1750–1890*, Eccles, 1977. A former child patient described their work, J. E. Phythian, 'Whitworth and its doctors fifty years ago', *Transactions of the Rochdale Literary and Scientific Society*, XII, 1914–16, pp. 55–66.
6 J. T. Slugg, *Reminiscences of Manchester Fifty Years Ago*, Manchester, 1881, p. 57.
7 John V. Pickstone, ' "Medical Botany" (self-help medicine in Victorian England)', *Memoirs and Proceedings of the Manchester Literary and Philosophical Society*, CXIC, 1976–77, pp. 90–1.
8 *Lancet*, 17 June 1882, p. 1002. The *Lancet* had numerous earlier references to 'Coffin poisons'.
9 *Macclesfield Mirror and Cheshire Record*, 9 May 1857.
10 J. K. Crellin, 'James Morison and his pills. A study of the nineteenth century pharmaceutical market', *Transactions of the British Society for the History of Pharmacy*, 4, 1974, p. 114.
11 P.P. 1844, IX, pp. 547–8.
12 P.P. 1854, XII, p. 588.
13 W. W. Gibson, 'Ardwick Sunday School Sick and Burial Society, 1827–36', MS, Papers of the Manchester Statistical Society, 1836–37.

14 *Report of Bury Friendly Society*, 1849; 'Rules and Tables of Bury Friendly Society'.
15 Haslingden Primitive Methodist Sunday School, quoted by C. Aspin, *Lancashire, the First Industrial Society*, p. 109.
16 Butterworth Diary, 10 June 1830.
17 Sunday School population estimated at 10,000. *Manchester Guardian*, 23 January 1847. A recent investigation has confirmed the Oldham estimate, i.e. one-fifth of the population of the town. C. E. Ward, 'Education as Social Control, Sunday Schools in Oldham, *c.* 1750–1850', unpublished M.A. thesis, University of Lancaster, 1975, p. 48.
18 J. Lea, 'Baptists and the Working Classes', in S. P. Bell, ed., *Victorian Lancashire*, Newton Abbot, 1974, p. 61.
19 For example, extract from *Report of St George's (Hulme) School Sick and Funeral Society*, 1846, 'Resolve then, each one, to give the best of your strength now to God and preserve, as far as you may, the vigour of your frame by wise moderation.'
20 John Roberton, *Observations*, p. 37.
21 P.P. 1844, XVII, Appendix, p. 48.
22 *Ibid.*, p. 49.
23 *Lancet*, 26 March 1842, p. 386.
24 Frederick Engels, *The Condition of the Working Class*, p. 171.
25 Report of investigation by physicians of the Manchester Clinical Hospital, *Lancet*, 30 April 1859, p. 447.
26 *First Address from the Committee*, Wigan Working Classes' Public Health Association, 1848, M.C.L.

V PHILANTHROPIC ENDEAVOUR

1 The house surgeon was 'considered responsible for the whole and the perfect order of each of them . . .'. *Report of the Committee of the Salford and Pendleton Royal Dispensary*, 1844–45, p. 9.
2 *Annual Report of the Bolton Infirmary*, 1855–56, p. 1.
3 Letter of M.O. of the Stockport Infirmary to Poor Law Commissioners, 30 January 1840, S.P.L. He described treating the Irish in cellar dwellings so packed that it was impossible to walk between the fever-stricken.
4 *Report of the Committee of the Salford and Pendleton Royal Hospital and Dispensary*, 1867, p. 6.
5 Admissions Register.
6 *Lancet*, 9 January 1841, p. 554.
7 *Ibid.*
8 Letter dated 30 March 1846 by Charles Royce, Royce Family Papers, M.C.L.
9 *Lancet*, 19 April 1862, p. 406.
10 Retrospective account in *Report of the General Committee upon the present condition of the Infirmary*, 1876, Manchester Royal Infirmary.
11 Florence Nightingale, *Notes on Hospitals*, London, 1863, pp. 5–6.
12 P.P. 1843, XIV, p. B22.
13 *Ibid.*, p. B23.
14 *Annual Report of the General Dispensary for Children*, 1843, p. 7.
15 *Ibid.*, 1850, p. 6.

16 Contemporary children's hospitals were established in Liverpool (1851), London (in Great Ormond Street in 1852), and Norwich (1854).

17 *Annual Report of the General Hospital and Dispensary for Sick Children*, 1855, p. 6.

18 *Ibid.*, 1878, p. 22.

19 *Ibid.*, 1857, p. 10.

20 *Ibid.*, 1857, p. 8.

21 *Ibid.*, 1860, p. 23.

22 *Ibid.*, 1868, p. 10.

23 *Ibid.*, 1860, pp. 6–7.

24 *Lancet*, 22 June 1861, p. 616.

25 *Report of the Board of Management of St Mary's Hospital*, 1864, p. 1.

26 Many of the German community are described in N. J. Frangopulo, 'Foreign communities in Victorian Manchester', *Manchester Review*, x, 1965, p. 196.

27 Florence Nightingale, *Notes on Hospitals*, p. iii.

28 *Annual Report of the Manchester Clinical Hospital*, 1856, p. 11.

29 *Annual Report of the Clinical Hospital and Dispensary for Children*, 1870, p. 9.

30 Committee Minute Book, Stockport Ragged and Industrial School, 11 April 1864.

31 *Ibid.*, 10 August 1863.

32 *Report of the Stockport Ragged and Industrial School*, 1861, p. 8.

33 P.P. 1871, VII, pp. 108–9.

34 *Ibid.*, p. 157.

35 According to evidence from the National Society, P.P. 1837–8, VII, p. 249.

36 P.P. 1854, LII, p. 820. The subject of the Preston schools as 'welfare agencies' is discussed in P. J. Dixon, 'School attendance in Preston: some socio-economic influences', in Roy Lowe, ed., *New Approaches to the Study of Popular Education, 1851–1902*, Occasional Publication, History of Education Society, IV, 1979, pp. 48–9.

37 *Report of the Manchester and Salford Education Aid Society*, 1865, pp. 10–11.

38 E.B., 'Popular Education and Political Economy' (extract from *Manchester Guardian*, n.d.), Scrapbook of Edward Brotherton.

39 Retrospective account in Arthur Ransome and William Royston, *Report upon the Health of Manchester and Salford during the last Fifteen Years*, Manchester and Salford Sanitary Association, 1867.

VI PUBLIC PROVISION

1 See Appendix II.

2 A school inspector wrote of the locality, 'there are some school rooms . . . where I catch myself a periodical cold as regularly as I attempt inspection'. P.P. 1854–55, XLII, p. 611. Churchmen resisted costly improvements. For example, the Bishop of Manchester objected to the requirement to board floors, 'for the convenience of children, many of whom, except in church, never stood on a boarded floor'. Press extract dated November 1861 in Archdeacon Rushton's Visitation Returns for Rusholme, M.C.L.

3 P.P. 1837, XXXI, p. 70.

4 *Ibid.*, p. 57.

5 P.P. 1859, XII, p. 189.

6 L. Horner, *On the Employment of Children in Factories and other Works in the United*

Kingdom and some Foreign Countries, London, 1840, pp. 9–10.
7   P.P. 1862, XXII, p. 251.
8   Letter to *Manchester Courier* by W. A. O'Connor (attributed to January 1866), Scrapbook of Edward Brotherton.
9   Adam Rushton, *My Life*, p. 28.
10 P.P. 1859, XII, p. 213.
11 P.P. 1844, IX, p. 543.
12 Quarterly Abstract, Manchester Union, December 1846.
13 P.P. 1844, XVII, Appendix, p. 47.
14 Report by Dr Joseph Blackshaw, M.O. of Stockport Union, 26 May 1841, to Poor Law Commissioners, Poor Law Union Papers.
15 *Ibid.*, Report by John Raynor, Surgeon to the Stockport Infirmary, 30 January 1840. He wrote, 'the poor . . . entertain the opinion that it is not only a safer but a more salutary protection'.
16 P.P. 1864, XXVIII, Appendix 3, p. 1.
17 P.P. 1842, XXXV, p. 207.
18 P.P. 1850, XLII, p. 106.
19 P.P. 1844, IX, p. 1066.
20 *Lancet*, 24 January 1863, pp. 100–1.
21 Rhodes Boyson, 'History of Poor Law Administration in North East Lancashire 1834–1871', unpublished M.A. thesis, University of Manchester, 1960, p. 43. The succeeding incidents are described pp. 404, 406.
22 Evidence by Stockport Guardians to Poor Law Commissioners, 26 May 1841.
23 P.P. 1849, XLII, p. 167.
24 Report of M.O. of Stockport Union to the Poor Law Commissioners, 13 July 1842.
25 P.P. 1867–8, LX, p. 144.
26 *Bolton Chronicle*, 23 January 1864.
27 P.P. 1841, XI, p. 136.
28 *Lancet*, 26 January and 2 February 1867, pp. 134, 167. Correspondence referred to the variety of remedies used in scald-head: nitrate of mercury ointment, iodine, sulphur, creosote, acetic acid, linseed meal poultices and scab painting with ink.
29 Order Book of Medical Officer of Heaton Norris in the Stockport Union, 1840, S.P.L.
30 C. Gardner, 'The Care of the Sick Poor of Preston in the Nineteenth Century', unpublished, 1967, p. 46, Preston Public Library.
31 *Lancet*, 11 April 1868, p. 489.
32 *Lancet*, 23 April 1870, pp. 587–8; 14 May 1870, p. 712; 4 June 1870, pp. 815–7.
33 P.P. 1844, XXXVIII, pp. 751–5.
34 P.P. 1846, XXXII, p. 289.
35 For example, Quarterly Abstract, Manchester Union, March 1852.
36 Committee Minute Book, Stockport Ragged and Industrial School, 11 June 1866.
37 James Kay-Shuttleworth, *Thoughts and Suggestions on certain Social Problems*, London, 1873, p. 66.
38 J. Bannister, *From Parish to Metro. Two Centuries of Local Government in a Lancashire Town*, Bury, 1974, p. 20.

III THE FACTORY AGE, 1870–1900

I CHILDREN AND INDUSTRY

1 D. A. Farnie, *The English Cotton Industry and the World Market, 1815–96*, London, 1979, pp. 309–10.
2 P.P. 1876, XVI, p. 25.
3 P.P. 1875, XVIII, Pt 2, pp. xli–ii.
4 Figures for the towns, as distinct from registration districts, calculated from statistics in *Reports of Registrar General*, P.P. 1877, XXV; 1897, XXI; 1902, XIV.
5 Retrospective account in *Annual Report on the Health of Blackburn*, 1897, pp. 3–4.
6 P.P. 1876, XVI, p. 261. Discussion of statistics, Edmund and Ruth Frow, *A Survey of the Half-time System in Education*, Manchester, 1970, pp. 27–8.
7 P.P. 1876, XXX, p. 480.
8 By the '80s all children in the age group were taught as half-timers. *Report of the Work of the Oldham School Board, 1885–8*, p. 36.
9 P.P. 1876, XVI, p. 296.
10 *Ibid.*, p. 301.
11 Evidence from N.U.T., Edmund and Ruth Frow, *The Half-time System*, p. 71.
12 K. P. C. Thorne, 'Development of Education in Chorley and District from 1800 to 1902', pp. 178, 181.
13 M. E. Young, 'The Burnley School Board, 1871–1890', unpublished. M.Ed. thesis, University of Manchester, 1973, p. 121.
14 Fred Blackburn, *George Tomlinson*, London, 1954, p. 12.
15 P.P. 1876, XXX, pp. 466, 491.
16 P.P. 1873, XXIV, p. 133.
17 P.P. 1873, LV, p. 53.
18 P.P. 1874, XIII, pp. 105–6.
19 P.P. 1876, XXX, p. 450.
20 'Memoranda of Quarry Bank Mill', p. 124.
21 *Annual Report of the Rochdale Infirmary and Dispensary for the Relief of the Sick Poor*, 1880, p. 12.
22 Evidence on tape, ' "Hurrah for a Life in the Factory". Experiences of Life in the Lancashire Cotton Towns before the First World War', unpublished, Department of Manchester Studies, Manchester Polytechnic.
23 Hilda Snowmen, *née* Snape, 'Autobiography', MS. p. 22, Bolton Public Library.
24 P.P. 1887, XXIX, p. 479.
25 *Lancet*, 1 May 1897, p. 1241.
26 Alice Foley, *A Bolton Childhood*, Manchester, 1973, p. 52.
27 *Report of the Medical Inspector of School Children, County Borough of Rochdale*, 1908, p. 7.
28 Nora Mills, 'Child growth under the half-time factory system', *Transactions of the Rochdale Literary and Scientific Society*, XVIII, 1932–34, p. 70.
29 P.P. 1876, XXX, p. 424.
30 P.P. 1873, XIX, p. 158.

II CHILDREN AND THE ENVIRONMENT

1 *Report on the Health of Bolton*, 1873, pp. 6, 8.
2 *Report of the M.O.H. of Ashton-under-Lyne*, 1899, p. v.
3 *Report of the M.O.H. of Oldham*, 1886, p. 12.
4 Quoted in Fred Scott, 'Conditions and Occupations of the People of Manchester and Salford', *Transactions of the Manchester Statistical Society*, 1888–89, p. 108.
5 Dancer's microscope used in 1868, R. H. Nuttall, 'Microscopes for Manchester', *Chemistry in Britain*, XVI, March 1980, p. 135.
6 Quoted by James Niven, *Report on the Health of Manchester*, 1897, p. 92.
7 James Niven, 'A note on a widespread source of infection generally disregarded', *Medical Chronicle*, IV, October 1895 to March 1897, pp. 348–9.
8 Evidence from early School Medical Officers' reports.
9 *Annual Report for the Year 1913 of the Chief Medical Officer of the Board of Education*, P.P. 1914–16, XVIII, p. 58.
10 For example, 'Medical Inspection of Schools', *Annual Report on the Health of Salford*, 1908, p. 129.
11 'Annual Report of the School M.O.', *Report on the Health of Bolton*, 1909, p. 110.
12 *Annual Report of the M.O.H. of Rochdale*, 1910, p. 15.
13 *Annual Report on the Health of Blackburn*, 1910, p. 41.
14 *Annual Report of the Chief M.O.H. for the Year 1889, County Palatine of Lancaster*, p. 13.
15 J. E. Mercer, 'The Conditions of Life in Angel Meadow', *Transactions of the Manchester Statistical Society*, 1896–97, p. 7.
16 Robert Roberts, *The Classic Slum* (Manchester, 1971), Harmondsworth, 1973, p. 78.
17 Robert Roberts, *A Ragged Schooling*, Manchester, 1976, p. 87.
18 Robert Roberts, *The Classic Slum*, p. 75.
19 Margaret Penn, *Manchester Fourteen Miles*, Cambridge, 1947, p. 105.
20 A condition which persisted. *Annual Report of the M.O.H. County Borough of Wigan*, 1913, p. 12.
21 *Annual Report of the M.O.H. for the Borough of Macclesfield, 1891*, p. 13.
22 *Annual Report on the Health of Blackburn*, 1891, p. 11.
23 *Annual Report of the M.O.H. for the Borough of Macclesfield*, 1873, pp. 18–9. He also pointed out that Liverpool, where women were not employed in factory labour, had currently a higher rate of mortality.
24 For mortality rates see p. 110.
25 *Annual Report of the M.O.H. for the County Borough of Stockport*, 1893, pp. 14–17. (Out of 2,341 births there were 482 deaths in the first month of life.)
26 *Ibid.*, 1889, p. 10.
27 Discussed in a later survey. P.P. 1914, XXXIX, pp. 19–24.
28 *Annual Report of the Officer of Health of Barton, Eccles, Winton and Monkton*, 1877, p. 14; *British Medical Journal*, 21 February 1880, p. 310.
29 *British Medical Journal*, 30 July 1892, p. 277.
30 *Annual Report on the Health of Blackburn*, 1889, p. 36.
31 *Report on the Health of Manchester*, 1910, p. 61.
32 *Annual Report on the Health of Blackburn*, 1908, p. 36.
33 James Niven, *Observations on the History of Public Health Effort in Manchester*, Manchester, 1923, p. 199.
34 Robert Montgomery, 'A Comparison of some of the Economic and Social

Conditions of Manchester and the surrounding Districts in 1834 and 1884', *Transactions of the Manchester Statistical Society*, 1884–85, p. 17.

35 *British Medical Journal*, 24 August 1872, p. 223.

36 Robert Roberts, *The Classic Slum*, p. 112.

37 *Annual Report of the Manchester Clinical Hospital and Dispensary for Children*, 1874, p. 8.

38 P.P. 1906, XLVII, II, p. 208.

39 Robert Roberts, *A Ragged Schooling*, p. 71.

40 Beatrice Webb, *My Apprenticeship*, London, 1929, pp. 165–6. Breakfasts would be taken to work.

41 Hilda Snowmen, *née* Snape, 'Autobiography', pp. 1–21.

42 *Ibid.*, p. 18.

43 Robert Roberts, *The Classic Slum*, p. 109.

44 Dr Henry Ashby, physician to the Manchester Children's Hospital, *Lancet*, 1 October 1904, p. 86.

45 P.P. 1904, XXXII, I, Appendix, p. 125.

46 Evidence from Rochdale, P.P. 1910, LII, p. 222.

47 Charles Creighton, *History of Epidemics in Britain* (1894), London, 1965, II, p. 767.

III CHILD MORTALITY AND DISEASE

1 Statistics extracted from *Reports of Registrar General*, P.P. 1896, XCIII, P.P. 1898, XVIII, and from M.O.H. reports in the municipalities.

2 P.P. 1909, CIII, p. 202. A Salford physician said, 'the amount [of lead plaster] used is simply enormous'. Other methods mentioned in oral evidence.

3 Robert Roberts, *The Classic Slum*, p. 127 n.

4 *Lancet*, 25 April 1903, pp. 1200–1.

5 *Annual Report of the General Hospital and Dispensary for Sick Children*, 1892, p. 14.

6 P.P. 1909, XXXIII, p. 87. Even ten years later there were references to the large number of midwives on official lists who were unable to write and thus unable to keep registers. *Report of M.O.H., County Palatine of Chester*, 1919, p. 25.

7 *Report of the M.O.H. for the County Borough of Stockport*, 1893, p. 17.

8 *Report of the M.O.H. on the Health of Bolton*, 1874, p. 7.

9 For example, 'Instructions delivered to every house in the Borough of Stalybridge', *Report of the M.O.H., County Palatine of Chester*, 1898, p. 8. (The infantile death rate in Stalybridge that year was 239 per 1,000.)

10 Henry Ashby, 'Infantile Mortality', *Transactions of the National Association for the Promotion of Social Science*, 1884, p. 503.

11 P.P. 1904, XXXII, II, p. 332.

12 T. C. Railton, 'Practice and precept in children's diseases', *Medical Chronicle*, III, April–September 1900, pp. 4–8.

13 *Annual Report of the General Hospital and Dispensary for Sick Children*, 1895, pp. 14–15.

14 P.P. 1890, XXIV, p. ix.

15 Robert Roberts, *The Classic Slum*, p. 112.

16 *Annual Report of the General Hospital and Dispensary for Sick Children*, 1895, p. 14.

17 Robert Roberts, *The Classic Slum*, p. 78–9.

18 National statistics summarised by Charles Porter, *Report of M.O.H. for 1895, County Borough of Stockport*, p. 25.

19 *Annual Report on the Health of Blackburn*, 1895, p. 28; *Report on the Health of Manchester*, 1895, p. 72.
20 James Niven, *Observations on the History of Public Health Effort*, p. 81.
21 *Annual Report on the Health of Salford*, 1879, p. 26. Notifiable by legislation of 1889.
22 *Lancet*, 30 August 1884, p. 376.
23 *Annual Report on the Health of Salford*, 1879, p. 24.
24 *Report of the Health Committee*, Borough of Bury, 27 January 1897.
25 *Lancet*, 15 January 1876, p. 108.
26 *Ibid.*, 2 September 1876, p. 339.
27 *Annual Report of the General Hospital and Dispensary for Sick Children*, 1880, p. 15.
28 *Annual Report of the Officer of Health of Barton, Eccles, Winton and Monkton*, 1889, p. 14.
29 *Annual Report of the Manchester Clinical Hospital and Dispensary for Children*, 1879, p. 8.
30 Minutes of the General Hospital and Dispensary for Sick Children, 4 November 1896.
31 P.P. 1883, XX, p. xvii.
32 P.P. 1904, XXXII, II, p. 328.
33 *Annual Report of the General Hospital and Dispensary for Sick Children*, 1862, p. 13.

IV FAMILY SELF-HELP

1 Robert Roberts, *The Classic Slum*, p. 124.
2 William Brockbank, *The Honorary Medical Staff of the Manchester Royal Infirmary, 1830–1945*, Manchester, 1965, p. 41.
3 P.P. 1914, IX, p. 613.
4 *Ibid.*, p. 113.
5 The Manchester coroner referred to cases where a qualified doctor had thirteen or fourteen surgeries with an unqualified man in each. *Lancet*, 2 February 1884, p. 216.
6 *Annual Report of the Officer of Health of Barton, Eccles, Winton and Monkton*, 1878, p. 1.
7 *Reports of the Chorlton-upon-Medlock Dispensary*, 1870, 1899.
8 *Report of the Chief School M.O.H., Cheshire County Council*, 1909, p. 27.
9 Numerous references. for example, '... I am strongly against you thuching (*sic*) my boys eyes in any shape or form. Leave them as they are. We have kept him all these years and will keep him longer ...' *Annual Report of the School M.O. of the Borough of Rochdale*, 1912, p. 3. Violence described in 'Medical Inspection of Schools', *Report of M.O.H. of the County Borough of Salford*, 1910, p. 90.
10 Weekly advertisement in the *Accrington Times* in the 1870s and '80s. The following advertisements are taken from the same source and also from the *Bolton Chronicle* and the *Stockport Advertiser*.
11 J. T. Slugg, *Reminiscences of Manchester Fifty Years Ago*, pp. 47, 60.
12 Ruth Johnson, *Old Road. A Lancashire Childhood*, Manchester, 1974, p. 89.
13 Robert Roberts, *The Classic Slum*, p. 125.
14 MSS., Admission Registers, Sick Club Payments, Medical Certificates of Bennett Street Sunday School Society, M.C.L.
15 P.P. 1874, XXIII, p. lvii.
16 *Annual Report of the General Hospital and Dispensary for Sick Children*, 1876, p. 11.
17 MSS., Admission Registers, etc., Sick and Burial Society of Stand (Whitefield)

Unitarian Sunday School and Chapel, M.C.L.

18　M. L. Davies, ed., *Life as we have known it*, London, 1977, p. 61.
19　Robert Roberts, *The Classic Slum*, p. 87.
20　*Annual Report of the M.O.H. for the Borough of Macclesfield*, 1890, p. 12.
21　Henry Ashby, 'Infantile Mortality', *Transactions of the National Association for the Promotion of Social Science*, 1884, p. 504.
22　*Annual Report of the General Hospital and Dispensary for Sick Children*, 1894, p. 14.
23　*Ibid.*, 1878, pp. 11–12.
24　Records of the Bollington No. 1 Union Burial Society, founded 1833, have recently been salvaged. I am indebted to Dr John Coope of Bollington for permission to use them.

V PHILANTHROPIC ENDEAVOUR

1　*Annual Report of the General Hospital and Dispensary for Sick Children*, 1873, p. 5.
2　*Report of St Mary's Hospital and Dispensary*, 1877, p. 5.
3　Described in the *Lancet*, 1 July 1871, p. 27.
4　Charles E. Smith, 'Reminiscences of the old Manchester Royal Infirmary in the early 'seventies', *Medical School Gazette*, November 1927, p. 14.
5　Register of Infectious Diseases, 5 July 1872.
6　*Lancet*, 1 July 1871, p. 27.
7　William Brockbank, *The Honorary Medical Staff of the Manchester Royal Infirmary*, p. 50.
8　For example, description of a cleft palate operation, *British Medical Journal*, 7 May 1864, p. 492.
9　*Annual Report of the Manchester Children's Hospital*, 1898, p. 21 (the official name change was in 1896).
10　*Ibid.*, 1912, p. 25.
11　*Lancet*, 21 January 1882, p. 128. The first anaesthetist (part-time) was not appointed till 1896.
12　Charles E. Smith, 'Reminiscences of the old Manchester Royal Infirmary', p. 13.
13　*Annual Report of the General Hospital and Dispensary for Sick Children*, 1875, p. 13. The fever ward was kept at high temperature. In some seasons 35 cwt of coal a week was used in the open fires, compared with 24 cwt in ordinary wards.
14　31 March 1877, Minutes of Monthly Meeting of the Board of Governors.
15　*Report of the Board of Management of St Mary's Hospital*, 1872, p. 4.
16　There were seventy cases of infantile paralysis in that year.
17　*Report of the General Hospital and Dispensary for Sick Children*, 1877, p. 21.
18　Robert Roberts, *A Ragged Schooling*, p. 68.
19　MS. Register of cases attended by the Nurse, Rochdale Parish Church, 1892–93, Rochdale Public Library.
20　Mary Stocks, *A Hundred Years of District Nursing*, London, 1960, p. 98.
21　Alderman Rumney, *Manchester Guardian*, 23 July 1868.

VI *SOCIAL DISCIPLINE AND PUBLIC PROVISION*

1 *Lancet*, 10 June 1876, p. 876.
2 Calculations were made of the amount of sulphuric acid per square mile in the vicinity of the Manchester Royal Infirmary, *Lancet*, 4 April 1891, p. 802.
3 *Lancet*, 30 July 1887, p. 240.
4 *Report on the Health of the County Borough of Stockport*, 1901, pp. 90–1.
5 *Report of M.O.H. of the Borough of Eccles*, 1894, p. 16.
6 Report of M.O.H., 1873–74, *City of Manchester Proceedings of the Council*, 1 April 1874, p. 202.
7 *Annual Report of the M.O.H. for the Borough of Macclesfield*, 1875, p. 8.
8 Barnes Hospital Death Registers, 1876–83. Monsall Fever Hospital, Registers of Inpatients, 1886–92. M.C.L. (Later references to Monsall are from these sources.)
9 *Lancet*, 1 September 1883, p. 841. Air was extracted by air pump.
10 Retrospective account, *Annual Report of the Medical Superintendent, Burnley Joint Hospital Board*, 1947, p. 19.
11 In Bolton sanitary inspectors tried to prevent parents going to work from infected households. *Lancet*, 28 July 1888, p. 177.
12 John Leigh, 'Report on the Infectious Diseases in Manchester', presented to the Health Committee, 19 December 1870, p. 19.
13 *Ibid.*, p. 18.
14 *Annual Report of the M.O.H. of Salford for the Year 1893*, p. 88.
15 Octavius Sturges, His definition was recorded in successive editions of leading medical textbooks, for example, William Osler, *Principles and Practice of Medicine*, London, 1912, p. 1068.
16 A. B. Robertson, 'Children, teachers and society: the overpressure controversy', *British Journal of Educational Studies*, XX, 1972, p. 323.
17 P.P., 1906, XC, pp. ii, 40–6.
18 J. H. Reynolds, 'Education and social activities', in L. M. Mather, ed., *Sir William Mather*, London, 1925, pp. 93–4.
19 James Niven of Manchester, P.P. 1909, XLI, p. 137.
20 P.P. 1909, XLI, p. 151.
21 *British Medical Journal*, 6 October 1894, p. 764.
22 P.P. 1909, XXXVII, Pt II, p. 783.
23 P.P. 1904, XXXII, II, p. 220.

CONCLUSION

1 The phrase is Mary Dendy's. P.P. 1906, XLVII, II, p. 205.
2 Nationally the birth rate had declined from 36·3 per 1,000 in 1876 to 28·9 in 1900.
3 P.P. 1904, XXXII, I, Appendix, p. 25.
4 *Ibid.*, II, p. 13.
5 *Ibid.*, II, p. 178.
6 *Ibid.*, II, p. 123.
7 James Niven, *Ibid.*, II, p. 258.
8 Edwin Waugh, *Lancashire Sketches*, p. 256.

9 'Medical Inspection of Schools and School Children', *Annual Report of the M.O.H. of Bolton*, 1912, p. 92.
10 Education Act, 1918. See Appendix II.
11 *Report of the Consultative Committee on the Primary School*, 1931, p. xxix.

APPENDIX I

GLOSSARY

TERMS RELATING TO THE COTTON INDUSTRY AND CHILDREN'S EMPLOYMENT

Processes	*Children's work*
1. Preparatory to spinning: (a) Willowing, scutching (breaking up and cleaning), (b) Carding (combing).	Carding room 'hands' (previously as card setters, i.e. fixing wire bristles on leather strips, work which persisted later in wool).
(c) Roving (rolling on spindles).	Bobbin doffers: removed and replaced bobbins at the roving frames.
2. Spinning (in early factories, on water frames or throstles, so called because their noise was like that of a thrush).	Scavengers: swept up the cotton waste, retrieved ends from under the mules. Piecers: tied broken threads (on the self-acting mule followed the carriage in and out).
3. Weaving.	Tenters: weavers' assistants: refilled shuttles, swept and cleaned.
4. Finishing: (a) Bleaching. (b) Dyeing. (c) Printing.	Keir boys: worked at the bleach vats. Dye boys. 'Teerers': spread colour for the block printers. Assistants to machine printers.

TERMS RELATING TO DISEASES OF CHILDREN
(Common infections are explained in the text)

Abscesses. Inflamed swellings which became open sores.

Atrophy. Wasting away.

Bronchitis. Chest disease which in a serious form became pneumonia.

Chilblains. Inflamed condition of the skin, particularly of hands and feet.

Chorea. St Vitus' Dance, nervous disease.

Croup. Throat disease caused by partial blockage of the larynx.

Convulsions. Fits, spasms, associated often with teething.

Deformities. Malformations, including cleft palate, club foot, hare lip.

Erysipelas. Infection from wounds and often following early surgery. (Also known as St Anthony's Fire.)

Hernia. Protruding organ which could be protected by a truss.

Hydrocephalus. Fluid on the brain.

Meningitis. Various forms, including tuberculous meningitis, inflammation of the membrane.

Ophthalmia. Inflammation of the eye. (Ophthalmia neonatorum, blindness due to purulent discharge at birth.)

Puerperal fever. Associated with child birth.

Rickets. Softened condition of the bones, the result of poor nutrition.

Ringworm. Fungus in the scalp.

Scald-head. Similar to ringworm.

Scrofula. Enlarged glands, sign of tuberculous constitution.

Scurvy. Skin disease due to lack of suitable food.

Strumous inflammation. Indicative of scrofulous condition.

Syphilis. Venereal disease which could be inherited.

Thrush. Disease of the tongue and throat caused by parasitic fungus and due to uncleanliness.

Tuberculosis. Of bones and joints and other forms, including abdominal (mesenteric) and pulmonary (phthisis), often following infectious diseases.

Typhoid fever. Enteric fever, result of poor sanitation, sewage pollution. (Distinguished by the mid-nineteenth century from typhus, disease associated with overcrowding.)

Ulcers. Open sores discharging pus.

APPENDIX II

SUMMARY OF LEGISLATION RELATING TO CHILDREN'S EMPLOYMENT IN TEXTILES

1802   42 Geo. III., c. 73. *The Health and Morals of Apprentices Act.* Restricted hours of work of apprentices in cotton factories and forbade night work.

1819   59 Geo. III., c. 66. *An Act for the Regulation of Cotton Mills and Factories.* Prohibited the employment of children under nine and night work of children in cotton factories.

1833   3 and 4 Will. IV., c. 103. *An Act to Regulate the Labour of Children and Young Persons in Mills and Factories.* Prohibited the employment of children under nine in textile factories (certain exceptions were made for silk factories). Between the ages of nine and thirteen children's work was restricted to forty-eight hours a week. Instruction was to be given for two hours each day. Provision for inspection ensured that the Act was carried out.

1844   7 and 8 Vict., c. 15. *An Act to amend the Laws relating to Labour in Factories.* The age limit for child workers was lowered to eight. Between eight and thirteen the work was restricted effectively to six and a half hours a day. More stringent educational regulations whereby children were to attend school three hours a day. Hours of work to be regulated by a public clock. Machinery was to be fenced and no child was allowed to clean it while in motion.

1845   8 and 9 Vict., c. 29. *Act to Regulate the Labour of Children in Calico Print Works.* Provided only partial protection, since for children between eight and thirteen school attendance was in terms of thirty days each half-year.

(Legislation between 1860 and 1870 extended the provisions of the 1844 Act to a variety of work places, including potteries, furnaces, foundries and printworks. Nationally, however, for the majority of children work was not restricted until education became compulsory following the Education Act of 1880.)

1874   37 and 38 Vict., c. 44. *An Act to make better Provision for improving the Health of Women, Young Persons and Children employed in Manufactures.* Prohibition of employment of children under nine (from 1875 under ten), and of full time employment under fourteen unless children had a certificate of educational proficiency, fixed at the fourth standard.

1891   54 and 55 Vict., c. 75. *An Act to amend the Law relating to Factories and Workshops.* Prohibition of employment of children under eleven. An employer should 'not knowingly allow a woman to be employed . . . within four weeks after she has given birth to a child'.

1901 1 Edw. VII., c. 22. *Factory and Workshop Consolidation Act.* Prohibition of employment of children under twelve.

1918 8 and 9 Geo. V., c. 39. Prohibited exemption from attendance at school between ages of five and fourteen (Half-time system officially ended when the Act came into operation in 1921.)

SELECT BIBLIOGRAPHY

PRIMARY SOURCES

MANUSCRIPT MATERIALS

(Infirmary sources are in the institutions. Other local sources are in the Archives Department of the Manchester Central Library, except where stated.)

Bills of Mortality. Archdeacon Rushton's Visitation Returns, 1846.

Board of Health in Manchester. Minutes 1831–32.

Burial ground registers. Manchester: General (Dissenters') Burial Ground, Rusholme, (from 1821). St John's Church, Deansgate. Salford: New Windsor Chapel, Salford Public Library.

Coroners' records. 'Register of Deaths in Stockport, 1851–56', Stockport Public Library.

Diaries. Butterworth Diary (1830–43), Oldham Public Library. William Rowbottom, 'Chronology or Annals of Oldham', Oldham Public Library.

Dispensaries, infirmaries. Bolton: Proceedings of the Committee of the Bolton Dispensary, 1813–19, Bolton Public Library. Manchester: Ardwick and Ancoats Dispensary, Minute Books, from 1873. General Dispensary for Children (later General Hospital and Dispensary for Sick Children), Minutes of Monthly Board Meetings, from 1865. Manchester Infirmary (later Manchester Royal Infirmary), Minutes of the Weekly Board, from 1752; Admission Registers from 1752; Death Registers of the Fever Hospital, 1858–72; Register of Infectious Diseases, from 1872. Monsall Fever Hospital, Admission Registers, 1886–92; Death Registers, 1876–83. Salford: Union Infirmary, Records of Visiting Committee, from 1880, Salford Public Library.

Family archives etc. Farrer Papers, Poor Relief Notebooks of Ann Ecroyd, 1819–43; Notebooks of the Relief Committee for districts within the township of Burnley, 1843. Royce Papers, Correspondence of Charles Royce. Scrapbook of Edward Brotherton, 1847–70. Hilda Snowmen, *née* Snape, Autobiography, Bolton Public Library.

Guardians' records. Poor Law Union Papers (Stockport), 1837–48, Stockport Public Library.

Indentures. Indenture Book, 1812–41, Bury Public Library. Indentures and Agreements, Quarry Bank, Styal, 1785–1846.

Prescriptions, etc. Heaton Norris Medical Order Book, 1840, Stockport Public Library. Physician's Prescription Book, Styal, 1804–27. Rochdale Parish Church Nurse, Notebook of Cases, 1892–93, Rochdale Public Library.

Schools. Archdeacon Rushton's Visitation Returns, 1846. Correspondence in National Society Letter Files relating to individual schools in union with the society. Minutes of the Committee of the Stockport Ragged and Industrial School, from 1852, Stockport Public Library.

Sick and burial societies. Bollington Burial Society (records from 1833 in private possession and unclassified): Admission Registers; Funeral Registers; Death Certificates. German Street (Manchester) Sunday School Sick and Burial Society: Admission Registers from 1829; Funeral Registers, 1829–32; Records of Sick Club Payments, 1842–83; Surgeons' Certificates, 1871–81. Stand (Whitefield) Unitarian Sunday School and Chapel Sick and Burial Society (records from 1867, not yet catalogued): Admission Registers; Registers of Subscriptions and Sickness Benefits; Confinement Accounts, 1877–80.

Surveys. Papers of the Manchester Statistical Society, 1834–40.

TYPESCRIPT MATERIALS

'Memoranda of Quarry Bank Mill from its commencement about 1794', Quarry Bank Mill.

Moses Heap, 'My Life and Times' (1824–1913), Rawtenstall Public Library.

PRINTED MATERIALS

1. Local

(Except where stated, local materials are in the Manchester Central Library. Hospital reports, however, have been consulted in the individual institutions or in the public libraries. Medical officers' reports are also in public libraries or postgraduate medical centres. The sequence of such reports has been taken from the earliest available, which is indicated.)

Board of Health. *Proceedings of the Board of Health in Manchester, 1796–1805. Reports of the Board of Health in Manchester,* 1809, 1825, 1834–36, 1839, 1851, University of Manchester.

Burial, friendly societies, etc. *Reports* of: Ardwick Sunday School Sick and Funeral Society, 1827–36; Bennett Street Sunday School Sick and Funeral Society, 1843; Bollington Burial Society, from 1833 (in private possession); Bury Friendly Society, 1843; St George's (Hulme) School Sick and Funeral Society, 1846.

Dispensaries, infirmaries. *Reports* of: Ardwick and Ancoats Dispensary, 1829; Blackburn General Dispensary, 1825; Bolton Dispensary, 1832; Burnley Victoria Hospital, 1886; Bury Dispensary, 1831; Chorley Dispensary, 1834; Chorlton upon Medlock Dispensary, 1832; Manchester Clinical Hospital, 1856; Manchester Eye Hospital, 1832; (Manchester) General Dispensary for Children, 1833; Manchester Infirmary, 1753; Manchester Lying-in Hospital, 1791; Oldham Infirmary, 1872; Preston Infirmary, 1877; Rochdale General Dispensary, 1833; Salford and Pendleton Dispensary, 1828; Stockport) Dispensary and General Infirmary, 1833.

Educational organisations. *Reports* of: Manchester and Salford Education Aid Society, 1865–70; Industrial Ragged School Bolton, 1861, Bolton Public Library; Manchester Ragged Schools, 1863–80 (miscellaneous issues covering a number of schools); Ragged and Industrial School, Salford, 1856–68; Ragged and Industrial School, Stockport, from 1855, Stockport Public Library; Rochdale Auxiliary

British and Foreign School Society, from 1834, Rochdale Public Library, Stockport Sunday School, from 1806, Stockport Public Library.

Provident, philanthropic societies, etc. *Reports* of: Burnley Ladies' Charity, 1820, 1843, Burnley Public Library; Manchester and Salford District Provident Society, from 1833; Manchester and Salford Sanitary Association, from 1853; Poor Children's Aid Committee, Rochdale, 1887, Rochdale Public Library; Wigan Working Classes' Public Health Association, 1848.

Public Health Committees. *Reports of medical officers:* Ashton under Lyne, 1878; Blackburn, 1889; Bolton 1873; Burnley, 1892; Bury, 1886; Eccles, 1874; Lancashire, 1889; Macclesfield, 1873; Manchester, 1868; Oldham, 1873; Preston, 1872; Rochdale, 1876; Salford, 1875; Stockport, 1882; Wigan 1879. Also *Reports by School Medical Officers* of the above municipalities and of Cheshire and Lancashire, prior to 1914.

Workhouse Unions. Burnley Union, Quarterly Abstracts, 1840. Manchester Union, Weekly Returns to Assistant Poor Law Commissioners from 1842; Lists of Infectious Diseases at Manchester Workhouse from 1853.

2. *National*
Official publications and reports

Minutes of Evidence taken before the Select Committee on the State of Children employed in the Manufactories of the United Kingdom, 1816, 111.

Reports of Factory Inquiry Commission, 1833, XX, XXI; 1834, XIX, XX.

Report from the Select Committee appointed to examine the Petitions presented from the Hand-loom Weavers, 1835, XIII.

Reports of Inspectors of Factories, beginning 1835, XL.

Report from the Select Committee appointed to consider the means of providing useful Education for the Children of the Poorer Classes, 1837–38, VII.

Annual Reports of the Registrar General for Births, Deaths, and Marriages in England and Wales, beginning 1839, XVI.

Reports from the Select Committee on the Act for the Regulation of Mills and Factories, 1840, X.

Report of the Assistant Commissioners on the Condition of the Hand-loom Weavers, 1840, XXIV.

Annual Reports of the Poor Law Commissioners, 1841, XI; 1842, XIX; 1849, XLVII; 1862, XXIV.

Reports from Commissioners Inquiring into Children's Employment, 1842, XVII; 1843, XIV, XV; 1862, XXIV.

Evidence taken, and Report made, by the Assistant Poor Law Commissioners sent to Inquire into the State of the Population of Stockport, 1842, XXXV.

Report from the Select Committee appointed to inquire into the Mode of administering Relief to the Sick Poor, 1844, IX.

Reports of Her Majesty's Inspectors of Schools, in *Minutes of the Committee of Council on Education*, 1844, XXXVIII; 1846, XXXII, 1849, XLII; 1850, LI, LII, 1854, XLIII; and in *Report of the Committee of Council on Education*, 1873, XXIV.

Reports of the Commissioners for Inquiring into the State of Large Towns and Populous Districts, 1844, XVII; 1845, XVIII.

Report from the Select Committee on Manchester and Salford Education, 1852, XI.

Report from the Select Committee appointed to inquire into the Mode in which Medical Relief is now administered in the different Unions, 1854, XII.

Reports of the Medical Officer of the Privy Council, 1860, **XXIX**; 1861, **XVI**; 1862, **XXII**; 1863, **XXV**; 1864, **XXVIII**.
Report of the Royal Sanitary Commissioners, 1868–9, **XXXII**.
Returns relating to Medical Poor Relief, 1870, **LVIII**.
Report from the Select Committee to inquire as to the best Means of preventing the Destruction of Lives of Infants, 1871, **VII**.
Report to the Local Government Board on proposed Changes in Hours and Ages of Employment in textile Factories, 1873, **LV**.
Report of the Commissioners into the working of the Factory and Workshops Acts, II, 1876, **XXX**.
Report of the Inter-departmental Committee on Physical Deterioration, I, II, 1904, **XXXII**.
Report of the Inter-departmental Committee on Medical Inspection and Feeding of Children attending Public Elementary Schools, 1906, **XLVII**.
Report on the work of the Central Midwives' Board, 1909, **XXXIII**.
Reports of the Commissioners on the Poor Laws and the Relief of Distress, 1909, **XXXVII**, **XLI**; *Minutes of Evidence*, 1910, **LII**, **LIV**.
Annual Reports of the Medical Officer of Health to the Local Government Board (Appendices on 'Infant and Child Mortality'), 1910, **XXXIX**; 1913, **XXXII**; 1914, **XXXIX**.
Report from the Select Committee to inquire into the Question of the Sale of Patent and Proprietary Medicines, 1914, **IX**.

3. Periodic publications, journals, etc.

Hansard.
Journal of the Statistical Society of London.
Memoirs and Proceedings of the Literary and Philosophical Society of Manchester.
Miscellaneous Papers of the Manchester Statistical Society.
Reports of the British Association for the Advancement of Science.
Transactions of the Lancashire and Cheshire Antiquarian Society.
Transactions of the Manchester Statistical Society.
Transactions of the National Association for the Promotion of Social Science.

British Medical Journal.
Health Journal and Record of Sanitary Engineering.
Health Lectures for the People, Manchester and Salford Sanitary Association.
Lancet.
Medical Chronicle.

Accrington Times.
Accrington Observer and Times.
Bolton Chronicle.
Macclesfield Mirror and Cheshire Record.
Manchester Chronicle.
Manchester Guardian.
Manchester Mercury.
Oldham Chronicle.
Stockport Advertiser.
Times.

4. Individual works

Adshead, Joseph, *Distress in Manchester. Evidence of the state of the labouring classes in 1840–42*, London, 1842.

Aikin, John, *A Description of the Country from thirty to forty Miles round Manchester*, London, 1795.

—*Thoughts on Hospitals*, London, 1771.

Ashby, Henry and Wright, G. A., *The Diseases of Children*, London, 1899.

Axon, W. E. A., *Annals of Manchester*, Manchester, 1886.

Baines, Edward, *History, Directory and Gazetteer of the County Palatine of Lancaster*, I, II, (Liverpool, 1824), reprinted Newton Abbot, 1968.

—*History of the Cotton Manufacture in Great Britain* (London, 1835), reprinted London, 1966.

Ballard, Dr, *Report on the Sanitary Condition of the Registration District of Bolton, Lancashire and particularly on its high Infant Mortality*, London, 1871.

Bamford, Samuel, *Early Days* (London, 1849), reprinted in W. H. Chaloner, ed., *The Autobiography of Samuel Bamford*, I, London, 1967.

—*Walks in South Lancashire* (Manchester, 1844), reprinted Hassocks, 1972.

Barlee, Ellen, *A Visit to Lancashire in December 1862*, London, 1863.

Battye, T., *Strictures upon the Churchwardens and Overseers of Manchester*, Manchester, 1801.

Black, James, 'Bolton and its neighbourhood, 1837,' *Transactions of the Provincial Medical and Surgical Association*, V, 1837.

Brierley, Ben, *Home Memories and Recollections of a Life*, Manchester, 1886.

Brown, J., *A Memoir of Robert Blincoe*, Manchester, 1832.

Butterworth, E., *A Statistical Sketch of the County Palatine of Lancaster*, (London, 1841), reprinted Manchester, 1968.

Chadwick, Edwin, *Report on the Sanitary Condition of the Labouring Population of Great Britain* (London, 1842), reprinted, M. W. Flinn, ed., Edinburgh, 1965.

Clerke, William, *Thoughts upon the Means of preserving the Health of the Poor by the prevention and suppression of epidemic fevers . . .*, London, 1790.

Creighton, Charles, *History of Epidemics in Britain*, II (Cambridge, 1894), reprinted London, 1965.

Dodd, William, *The Factory System Illustrated* (London, 1842), reprinted London, 1968.

Engels, Frederick, *The Condition of the Working Class in England* (London, 1892), reprinted London, 1969.

Farr, W., *Mortality in Mid-nineteenth century Britain* (London, 1837), reprinted London, 1974.

Faucher, Leon, *Manchester in 1844*, London, 1844.

Ferriar, John, *Medical Histories and Reflections*, I, II, London, 1810.

Fielden, John, *The Curse of the Factory System* (London, 1836), reprinted London, 1967.

Gaskell, Elizabeth, *Mary Barton* (London 1848), reprinted London, 1966.

Gaskell, Peter, *Artisans and Machinery* (London, 1836), reprinted London, 1968.

Gaulter, Henry, *Origin and Progress of the Malignant Cholera in Manchester*, London, 1833.

Greg, R. H., *The Factory Question considered in relation to its effects on the Health and Morals of those Employed in the Factories*, London, 1837.

Horner, L., *On the Employment of Children in Factories and other Works in the United Kingdom and in some Foreign Countries*, London, 1840.

Kay-Shuttleworth, James, *Four Periods of Public Education as reviewed in 1832–1839–1846–1862*, London, 1862.

Lee, William, *Report to the General Board of Health on a Preliminary Inquiry into the Sewerage, Drainage, and Supply of Water and the Sanitary Condition of the Inhabitants of Bacup*, London, 1849.

Leigh, John, and Gardiner, Ner, *History of the Cholera in Manchester in 1849*, London, 1850.

The Letters of Mrs Gaskell, J. A. V. Chapple and Arthur Pollard, eds., Manchester, 1966.

Newman, George, *Infant Mortality*, London, 1906.

Nightingale, Florence, *Notes on Hospitals*, London, 1863.

—*Notes on Nursing*, London, 1859.

Niven, James, *Observations on the History of Public Health Effort in Manchester*, Manchester, 1923.

Parochial Chapelry of Colne Burial Register, 1790–1812, Wilfred M. Spenser, ed., Nelson, 1968.

Percival, Thomas, *Essays Medical, Philosophical, and Experimental*, I, II, London, 1789.

Ranger, William, *Report to the General Board of Health on a Preliminary Inquiry into the Sewerage, Drainage, Supply of Water and the Sanitary Condition of the Inhabitants of the Township of Dukinfield*, London, 1856.

Rawlinson, Robert, *Report to the General Board of Health on a Preliminary Inquiry into the Sewerage, Drainage and Supply of Water and the Sanitary Condition of the Inhabitants of the township of Barton-upon-Irwell*, London, 1852.

Razzell, P. E., and Wainwright, R. W., eds. *The Victorian Working Class. Selections from Letters to the Morning Chronicle*, London, 1973.

Reach, A. B., *Manchester and the Textile Districts in 1849*, C. Aspin, ed., Helmshore, 1972.

Roberton, John, *Observations on the Mortality and Physical Management of Children*, London, 1827.

Rushton, Adam, *My Life as a Farmer's Boy, Factory Lad, Teacher and Preacher*, Manchester, 1909.

Senior, Nassau, W., *Letters on the Factory Act as it affects the Cotton Manufacture*, London, 1837.

Shaw, Charles, *Replies of Sir Charles Shaw to Lord Ashley M.P. regarding the Education, and Moral and Physical Condition of the Labouring Classes*, London, 1843.

Simon, John, *Public Health Reports*, I, II, London, 1887.

Slugg, J. T., *Reminiscences of Manchester Fifty Years Ago*, Manchester, 1881.

Taylor, W. Cooke, *Notes of a Tour in the Manufacturing Districts of Lancashire* (London, 1842), reprinted London, 1968.

Ure, Andrew, *The Philosophy of Manufactures* (London, 1836), reprinted London, 1967.

Wade, Richard, *Sketch of the Origin and Progress of the Lower Mosley Street Day and Sunday Schools by an Old Scholar*, Manchester, 1867.

Watts, John, *The Facts of the Cotton Famine*, London, 1866.

Waugh, Edwin, *Lancashire Sketches*, I, II, Manchester, 1892.

White, Charles, *A Treatise on the Management of Pregnant and Lying-in Women*, London, 1777.

Whitehead, James, *Notes on the Rate of Mortality in Manchester*, Manchester, 1863.

ORAL EVIDENCE

Private investigation in Rochdale, Hyde and Stalybridge.

'*Hurrah for a Life in the Factory', Experiences of Life in the Lancashire Cotton Towns before the First World War*, tapes and transcripts assembled in unit, Department of Manchester Studies, Manchester Polytechnic.

SECONDARY SOURCES

This section is not comprehensive. Other sources, less frequently used, are referred to in footnotes.

Abel-Smith, Brian, *The Hospitals, 1800–1948*, London, 1964.

Anderson, Michael, *Family Structure in Nineteenth Century Lancashire*, Cambridge, 1971.

—'Household structure and the industrial revolution; mid-nineteenth-century Preston in comparative perspective', in Peter Laslett, ed., *Household and Family in Past Time*, Cambridge, 1972.

Ashton, T. S., *Economic and Social Investigations in Manchester, 1833–1933* (London, 1934), reprinted Hassocks, 1977.

—'The standard of life of the workers in England, 1790–1830' in F. A. Hayek, ed., *Capitalism and the Historians*, London, 1954.

Bell, S. P., ed., *Victorian Lancashire*, Newton Abbot, 1974.

Bennett, W., *History of Burnley*, III, Burnley, 1948.

Boyson, Rhodes, *The Ashworth Cotton Enterprise*, Oxford, 1970.

—'The history of Poor Law administration in north-east Lancashire, 1834–71', M.A. thesis, University of Manchester, 1960.

Bridie, John W., *A Short History of St Mary's Hospital, Manchester, and the Honorary Medical Staff*, Manchester, 1922.

Brockbank, E. M., *Sketches of the Lives and Work of the Honorary Medical Staff of the Manchester Infirmary from its Foundation in 1752 to 1830*, Manchester, 1904.

Brockbank, William, *The Honorary Medical Staff of the Manchester Royal Infirmary, 1830–1945*, Manchester, 1965.

Brockington, C. Fraser, *A Short History of Public Health*, London, 1956.

Burnett, John, *Plenty and Want. A social history of diet in England from 1815 to the present day*, London, 1966.

Burney, Lester, *Cross Street Chapel Schools, Manchester, 1734–1942*, Manchester, 1977.

Bythell, Duncan, *The Handloom Weavers. A Study in the English Cotton Industry during the Industrial Revolution*, Cambridge, 1969.

Chapman, S. D., *The Early Factory Masters*, Newton Abbot, 1967.

Clarkson, Leslie, *Death, Disease and Famine in Pre-industrial England*, London, 1975.

Collier, Frances, *The Family Economy of the Working Classes in the Cotton Industry, 1784–1833*, Manchester, 1965.

Cullen, M. J., *The Statistical Movement in Early Victorian Britain*, Hassocks, 1975.

Davies, C. Stella, ed., *A History of Macclesfield*, Manchester, 1968.

Davies, C. Stella, *North Country Bred*, London, 1963.

Drummond, J. C. and Wilbraham, A., *The Englishman's Food. A History of Five Centuries of English Diet*, London, 1939.

Farnie, D. A., *The English Cotton Industry and the World Market, 1815–1896*, Oxford, 1979.

Flinn, M. W., 'Medical services and the New Poor Law', in Derek Fraser, ed., *The New Poor Law in the Nineteenth Century*, London, 1976.

Foley, Alice, *A Bolton Childhood*, Manchester, 1973.

Foster, John, *Class Struggle in the Industrial Revolution. Early industrial capitalism in three English towns*, London, 1974.

Frow, Edmund and Ruth, *A Survey of the Half-time System in Education*, Manchester, 1970.

Harte, N. B., and Ponting, K. G., eds., *Textile History and Economic History*, Manchester, 1973.

Henderson, W. O., *The Lancashire Cotton Famine, 1861–65*, Manchester, 1969.

Hewitt, Margaret, *Wives and Mothers in Victorian Industry*, London, 1958.

Hindle, G. B., *Provision for the Relief of the Poor in Manchester 1754–1826*, Manchester, 1975.

Hodgkinson, Ruth G., *Origins of the National Health Service*, London, 1967.

Hutchins, B. L., and Harrison, A., *A History of Factory Legislation*, London, 1926.

Johnson, Ruth, *Old Road. A Lancashire Childhood, 1912–26*, Manchester, 1974.

Lacquer, T. W., *Religion and Respectability. Sunday Schools and Working Class Culture 1780–1850*, Yale, 1976.

Lambert, R. J., 'A Victorian National Health Service: State vaccination, 1855–71', *Historical Journal*, V, 1962.

Lazenby, Walter, 'The social and economic history of Styal', M.A. thesis, University of Manchester, 1949.

Lee, C. H., *A Cotton Enterprise, 1795–1840. A History of M'Connell & Kennedy, Fine Cotton Spinners*, Manchester, 1972.

Leech, E. B., 'Early medicine and quackery in Lancashire', *Medico-chirurgical Journal*, XLVI, 1938.

Lewis, R. A., *Edwin Chadwick and the Public Health Movement, 1832–54*, London, 1952.

McKeown, T., and Record, R. G., 'Reasons for the decline of mortality in England and Wales during the nineteenth century', in M. W. Flinn and T. C. Smout, eds., *Essays in Social History*, Oxford, 1974.

Maltby, S. E., *Manchester and the Movement for National Elementary Education 1800–1870*, Manchester, 1918.

Mathias, P., *The First Industrial Nation*, London, 1969.

Midwinter, E. C., *Social Administration in Lancashire, 1830–1860*, Manchester, 1969.

Morris, R. J., *Cholera 1832*, London, 1976.

Neff, W. F., *Victorian Working Women*, London, 1966.

Pelling, M., *Cholera, Fever and English Medicine, 1825–1865*, Oxford, 1978.

Penn, Margaret, *Manchester Fourteen Miles*, Cambridge, 1947.

Pinchbeck, Ivy, and Hewitt, Margaret, *Children in English Society*, II, London, 1973.

Roberts, Robert, *A Ragged Schooling*, Manchester, 1976.

—*The Classic Slum* (Manchester, 1971), reprinted Harmondsworth, 1973.

Sigsworth, E. M., 'Gateways to death? Medicine, hospitals and mortality, 1700–1850', in P. Mathias, ed., *Science and Society*, Cambridge, 1972.

Smelser, N. J., *Social Change in the Industrial Revolution. An Application of Theory to the Lancashire Cotton Industry, 1770–1840*, London, 1959.

Smith, F. B., *The People's Health, 1830–1910*, London, 1979.

Thomis, M. I., *The Town Labourer and the Industrial Revolution*, London, 1974.

Thorne, K. P. C., 'The development of education in Chorley and district from 1800 to 1902', M.Litt. thesis, University of Lancaster, 1970.

Todd, F. A., 'The condition of the working class in Preston, 1790–1855', M.Litt. thesis, University of Lancaster, 1972.

Unwin, George, *Samuel Oldknow and the Arkwrights. The Industrial Revolution at Stockport and Marple*, London, 1924.

Wadsworth, A. P., and Mann, J. De Lacy, *The Cotton Trade and Industrial Lancashire, 1600–1780*, Manchester, 1965.

Walker, J. E. M., 'Environment and health in Manchester 1750–1850', PhD thesis, UMIST, 1975.

Ward, C. E., 'Education as social control. Sunday schools in Oldham, *c.* 1750–1850', MA thesis, University of Lancaster, 1975.

West, John L., *The Taylors of Lancashire, Bone Setters and Doctors, 1750–1890*, Eccles, 1977.

Wohl, Anthony, S., ed., *The Victorian Family*, London, 1978.

Woodward, John, and Richards, David, *Health Care and Popular Medicine in Nineteenth Century England*, London, 1977.

Woodward, John, *To do the sick no harm*, London, 1974.

INDEX